The War of
ARMAGEDDON

By Ernest Angley

ARMAGEDDON

PROLOGUE

You are about to read the most profound story about the Rapture, the Tribulation Period and the Battle of Armageddon ever written. Never before has such a novel been published that is based 100% on biblical truth, and the results are shocking.

"Armageddon" is a sequel to Ernest Angley's first novel, "Raptured," which has already changed the lives of thousands of people since it was published in 1950. Through many hours of seeking God in prayer, fasting and studying the Word, the Lord's humble prophet, Ernest Angley, received this revealing story from the Lord as a final warning of what is to come. You must heed the solemn warning contained in its pages, or you will find yourself to be one of its characters in living reality...and you will forever regret having to endure such torment, death and destruction.

With a heart for lost souls and in all humility, Ernest Angley presents the Lord's message to the world in "Armageddon."

CHAPTER
ONE

I t's an early spring morning, the frosty air still crisp with the winter chill that has not completely taken its departure. The sun is just beginning to peep over the hills and bid a cheery good morning to old Mother Earth. The smell of spring scents the air, and the birds are singing so loudly that it seems their throats will burst with joy.

It's just prior to "wake-up" time for many people in the city of Alabesta when an unbelievably shocking event rocks the city…

Suddenly, hundreds of people disappear into thin air. Had they all been in one place, the mystery of their disappearance wouldn't be so confusing; but people have vanished from every section of the city. Those left behind are completely shocked and bewildered that such a devastating catastrophe could have stricken their city.

Many went to sleep Sunday night beside their loved ones and awakened Monday morning to discover that their companions or children have vanished into thin air, taking nothing with them. Nearly every home in the city is affected, either directly or indirectly, because all the babies and small children are gone; not one is left. In some homes, the husband has vanished and the wife is left; in others, the wife is taken and the husband left.

The city has turned into a scene of utter chaos! Because drivers suddenly vanished from their cars, thousands of accidents have turned every road into a parking lot. Trains left without engineers have plowed through forests and neighborhoods, and airplanes with missing pilots have crashed to the ground.

The scene is the same all over the world, and the inhabitants of the Earth are dumbfounded!

Mass hysteria has broken out throughout the world as hysterical people fill the streets, frantically searching for missing loved ones but finding none.

Breaking news bulletins dominate the airwaves as dazed and confused TV and radio newscasters announce the unbelievable: "Like magic, thousands of people vanished from the face of the Earth about six o'clock this morning! Not law enforcement officers, the president or even the FBI can explain the greatest mystery ever to take place in the history of mankind!"

What could have possibly happened in the universe to cause so many people to disappear without warning and leave behind no trace or clue as to their whereabouts? So many people are filled with questions while others are coming up with thousands of speculations and bizarre theories as to what has happened to all of these people.

Only yesterday, Polly Gilmore had sat in her beloved church and heard the preacher say, "The Rapture is about to take place!" Those words had made her sit up a little straighter in her pew and fasten her eyes on the speaker's face, listening intently so as not to miss a word of what he had to say.

As she sat listening, Polly thought about her husband, Barry; she had always felt such a great burden for his soul. He kept promising her that he would start going to church again. In fact, he had promised her even before they were married that he would live for the Lord after their wedding; but he never kept his promise, and they now had three small children to raise. The thought of Barry being left when Jesus came troubled her even more as she had listened to the preacher tell of the end-time prophecies.

Polly knew without a doubt she was ready to meet the Lord and that she and their three children would be on the one flight out, but what would happen to poor Barry? She loved him so much; and although he had not kept his promise to get right with the Lord and serve Him, he had always been good to her and the children. They were comfortable and had a good life, but she knew there was much more to life than that. The greatest need in

Barry's life was Jesus. She believed in her heart that Barry did intend to live for the Lord some day, but it was such a dangerous time for him to keep putting the Lord off; and she was afraid he would wait too long.

The end-time message Polly had heard had been part of a weekend revival at Fairview Church that featured a young preacher, Leo Maspero. He had spoken with scholarly confidence, and his voice rang with the Spirit and the power of God. "In the Old Testament, the God of Heaven promised the Jews that He would gather them back to the Holy Land. Since 1921, the greatest gathering in the history of the Jews had been taking place; and in 1948, the Jews at last became a nation once again.

"Dear Friends, as I read how the Jews have fought for Israel, I realize the coming of the Son of God is very near. As we look for the Son of God to make His appearance in midair and for the Church—the Bride of Christ— to be raptured, the Jews are looking for the Redeemer of Israel. They are expecting Him to come to set up an earthly kingdom.

"Christ made His appearance almost 2000 years ago; however, when He was born, people said He was not the Son of God but an imposter. The prophets of old—Moses, Isaiah and others—spoke of His coming, so their unbelief was not because He came at an unexpected time; it was because His birth was too humble for them. They could not believe their King would be born in an ox stall and laid in a manger; and they shouted, **Let Him be crucified...and...His blood be on us, and on our children** (Matthew 27:22,25). In ignorance, the Jews crucified their King, the Son of the Most High.

"Today, the Jews are still looking for their Messiah; but there is a Man of Sin, a false christ, who is about to appear and who will possess all the characteristics that the Jews expect of their Messiah. When he makes his appearance, the Jews will accept him as their Christ."

As Polly listened, her mind had wandered to the trouble in the Middle East and the reports she had read in the newspapers. Such things made her feel weak, and her heart ached within because of Barry's condition. She knew she was ready to go. She loved the Lord and desired to be with Him, but Barry was not ready to meet his Lord. She knew how horrible it would be if he were left behind to suffer the tortures of the Tribulation or take the Mark of the Beast...Oh, no! Not that! He must get saved!

The young preacher had continued, "In the sixth chapter of Revelation, John said he saw the Lamb open one of the seals and a rider on a white horse go forth with a bow in his hand; **and a crown was given unto him: and he went forth conquering, and to conquer** (Revelation 6:2).

"Some people think this is Christ because the rider is on a white horse, but this cannot be Christ," Rev. Maspero explained, "because the Lamb—Christ—is the One who will open the seal.

"You may ask, 'Isn't white a symbol of peace?'

"Yes, white is a symbol of peace; and when the Antichrist comes, he will come claiming to be a peaceful king. **But he shall come**

in peaceably, and obtain the kingdom by flatteries (Daniel 11:21).

"When we say the word 'Rapture,' we mean the time when the Son of God makes His appearance in midair and the Bride of Christ, the Church, will be caught up to be with Him. **For the Lord himself shall descend from heaven with a shout, with the voice of the archangel, and with the trump of God: and the dead in Christ shall rise first: Then we which are alive and remain shall be caught up together with them in the clouds, to meet the Lord in the air: and so shall we ever be with the Lord** (I Thessalonians 4:16,17).

"Some may wonder or want to know when this Antichrist will come. Well, in the ninth chapter of Daniel, it's recorded that Daniel was praying and wanted to know what was going to happen to his people, the Jews. As he fasted, prayed and confessed their sins, he received this answer from Heaven: **Seventy weeks are determined upon thy people** (Daniel 9:24).

"We understand these not to be ordinary

weeks but weeks of years. Sixty-nine of those weeks of years were fulfilled up to the Crucifixion of Christ. The Jewish Dispensation closed and the Gentile Dispensation began. That means that the Jews have one more week of years, or seven years, to complete the seventy weeks declared to them in the Book of Daniel; but that time can't begin until the end of the Gentile Dispensation. The Rapture of the Bride will bring this Gentile Dispensation to a close, and then the Jews' final seven years will begin.

"You may think that the Church will go through half of the Tribulation, but that can't be true according to the Word of God. Isaiah says, **Come, my people, enter thou into thy chambers, and shut thy doors about thee: hide thyself as it were for a little moment, until the indignation be overpast** (Isaiah 26:20).

"In the Book of Revelation, one of the seven churches was promised that it would be delivered from the hour of temptation that is coming upon the Earth. **Because thou hast kept the word of my patience, I also**

will keep thee from the hour of temptation, which shall come upon all the world,
to try them that dwell upon the earth
(Revelation 3:10).

"It's not logical for the Gentile Bride to be
left here after the Gentile Dispensation has
come to a close. If we were to go through
half of the Tribulation Period, all we would
have to do is wait until the Man of Sin made
his appearance and count three-and-a-half
years; then we would know when the Son of
God would make His appearance and rapture
the Church. That's not in accordance with
Scripture. Jesus said no one—not even the
angels in Heaven—will know the day or the
hour of the coming of the Son of God. **But
of that day and hour knoweth no man, no,
not the angels of heaven, but my Father
only** (Matthew 24:36).

"The spirit of the Antichrist is already here,
but he cannot be revealed until the Church is
gone. I think of the Church as a dam holding back water. The Church is keeping the
Antichrist from making his appearance; but
when the Church is removed, the Antichrist

will rush in and take over.

"One of the first things he'll do is make a covenant with the Jews for seven years. **And he shall confirm the covenant with many for one week** (Daniel 9:27). Everything that must be fulfilled before the Rapture can take place has been fulfilled with regard to the gathering back of the Jewish people to their promised land.

"It looks as if the coming of the Lord is so very near," Rev. Maspero had declared. "The signs pointing to His coming have been fulfilled, and He could come any time and not do an injustice to the Holy Scriptures. Who knows? It might be today!"

Barry had been out of town on business during the revival, so he could not attend with Polly and the children. Each service, Polly would take notes about the revival prophecies that the young evangelist gave in his lectures; and she would leave them on the coffee table, praying that Barry would pick them up and read them. She didn't want to preach to him because she knew that would never work.

On Sunday afternoon, Polly had carefully

checked her notes, not knowing it would be the last day before Jesus would come; then she and the children went to church that evening. When she got home, she had again checked her notes from that evening's message and then left them on the coffee table.

As Polly got ready for bed, she thought about all of the things she had read in the book of Revelation and the book of Daniel. The study of the Antichrist had always interested her, and this young man had made it plainer than anyone she had ever heard. He had made Jesus' coming feel so close that it seemed every sinner in the building should have surrendered to the Lord before leaving the service.

Before Polly had drifted off to sleep, her mind went back to some more of the preacher's words. "The Antichrist will reveal himself, and the covenant will be made with the Jews. The Jews will rejoice; and no doubt, the bands will play as the Jews march for joy. Remember, they have been looking a long time for this great event. They will erect their temple in Israel and offer their sacrifices to

God as their forefathers did.

"I have been told that the Jews already have their stones hewn out and waiting so they can erect their temple as soon as their Messiah makes his appearance. That means they will have their temple erected in just a short time, and it will be ready for them to offer their sacrifices.

"We might call this man the Little Horn, that Wicked One, the Beast, the Son of Perdition, or other such names and still be talking about the same person. The Bible gives him a number of different names.

"He will cause craft to prosper, which means factories and all types of industries will flourish. The Antichrist will also do something his forefathers did not do—he will divide the spoil with the people, and that will make it even more convincing to many that he is the Son of God. **He shall enter peaceably even upon the fattest places of the province; and he shall do that which his fathers have not done, nor his fathers' fathers; he shall scatter among them the prey, and spoil, and riches** (Daniel 11:24).

"Hitler manifested such great power that some thought he would be the Antichrist, but Hitler could not have been the Messiah of the Jews because he did not favor the Jews. The Antichrist will favor the Jews above all other people, but Hitler had them killed by the millions.

"The first three-and-a-half years of the Tribulation Period will be a peaceful reign, and the Jews will offer their sacrifices to God; but after that time, everything will change. One day, the Jews will go up to the temple to worship and discover that the Antichrist has defiled the temple with some unholy sacrifice and set himself up in the temple of God, showing himself to be God. Up until that time, the Jews will not have believed the Antichrist to be God, but the Son of God; and their eyes will be opened.

"Suddenly, they'll realize that they have been deceived. **And in the midst of the week he shall cause the sacrifice and the oblation to cease** (Daniel 9:27). **And from the time that the daily sacrifice shall be taken away, and the abomination that** maketh desolate set up, there shall be a thousand two hundred and ninety days (Daniel 12:11). **When ye therefore shall see the abomination of desolation, spoken of by Daniel the prophet, stand in the holy place, (whoso readeth, let him understand:) Then let them which be in Judaea flee into the mountains** (Matthew 24:15,16). **Let no man deceive you by any means: for that day shall not come, except there come a falling away first, and that man of sin be revealed, the son of perdition; Who opposeth and exalteth himself above all that is called God, or that is worshipped; so that he as God sitteth in the temple of God, shewing himself that he is God** (II Thessalonians 2:3,4).

"A portion of the Jews will flee to the wilderness where God has a place of refuge prepared for them away from the Antichrist. **And there appeared a great wonder in heaven; a woman clothed with the sun, and the moon under her feet, and upon her head a crown of twelve stars: And she being with child cried, travailing in birth, and** pained to be delivered. And there appeared another wonder in heaven; and behold a great red dragon, having seven heads and ten horns, and seven crowns upon his heads. And his tail drew the third part of the stars of heaven, and did cast them to the earth: and the dragon stood before the woman which was ready to be delivered, for to devour her child as soon as it was born. And she brought forth a man child, who was to rule all nations with a rod of iron: and her child was caught up unto God, and to his throne. And the woman fled into the wilderness, where she hath a place prepared of God, that they should feed her there a thousand two hundred and threescore days (Revelation 12:1–6).

"In the thirteenth chapter of Revelation, John said, And I stood upon the sand of the sea, and saw a beast rise up out of the sea, having seven heads and ten horns, and upon his horns ten crowns, and upon his heads the name of blasphemy. And the beast which I saw was like unto a leopard, and his feet were as the feet of a bear, and

his mouth as the mouth of a lion: and the dragon gave him his power, and his seat, and great authority (Revelation 13:1,2). In other words, John said he saw a man rise up out of the nations. This is the Antichrist with his deceiving, governmental power.

"In that same chapter, John goes on to say that all the world will wonder after the Beast and worship him and that they will also worship the dragon, or the devil, who gave power unto the Beast. **And all the world wondered after the beast. And they worshipped the dragon which gave power unto the beast: and they worshipped the beast, saying, Who is like unto the beast? who is able to make war with him** (Revelation 13:3,4)?

"Later in that chapter, we see another Beast come forth. John said he had two horns like a lamb; he spake as a dragon, and he had power to call down fire from Heaven. This is the third member who will make up the Antigodhead. **And I beheld another beast coming up out of the earth; and he had two horns like a lamb, and he spake as a dragon. And he exerciseth all the power of** the first beast before him, and causeth the earth and them which dwell therein to worship the first beast, whose deadly wound was healed. And he doeth great wonders, so that he maketh fire come down from heaven on the earth in the sight of men (Revelation 13:11–13).

"In the Trinity of the Godhead, we have the Father, the Son and the Holy Ghost. The Antigodhead includes the devil, who is the Antigod; the Antichrist, who is the Beast; and the Antispirit, who is the False Prophet.

"Today, we're in the Holy Ghost Dispensation; and the Holy Ghost works in the interest of Christ. He is not working to glorify Himself but the Father and the Son. During the Tribulation, the Antispirit will be working to glorify the Antichrist and the devil. He will deceive men with the many great miracles he is able to perform and will tell those who dwell on the Earth that they must make an image of the Beast to worship. **And he had power to give life unto the image of the beast, that the image of the beast should both speak, and cause that as many as would**

not worship the image of the beast should be killed. And he causeth all, both small and great, rich and poor, free and bond, to receive a mark in their right hand, or in their foreheads (Revelation 13:15,16).

"Let me persuade you to make preparation to meet your Lord today because He may appear before another sunrise. **Watch therefore, for ye know neither the day nor the hour wherein the Son of man cometh** (Matthew 25:13)."

A hush lingered over the audience, and everything was deathly still as the minister closed his Bible. Then the choir began to sing, "Tomorrow May Mean Goodbye"; and the congregation stood for what Rev. Maspero said could be the last altar-call invitation for salvation before the Rapture. Conviction had gripped the hearts of many of the people, and some wept aloud before the Lord.

Polly had felt God's Spirit covering the church in a special way that day, and numbers of convicted people went for prayer. Nevertheless, others stood back, determined not to seek God in that service. They thought they would accept Him sometime later but not that evening.

When Rev. Maspero had given the last glorious testimony of those who had found Jesus, the congregation was dismissed. The people were filled with joy and praise to God for bringing so many into the fold; and as they passed slowly out of the church in groups of two or three, they were still talking about the wonderful service and how near the coming of the Lord must be.

CHAPTER
TWO

B arry Gilmore travels often in his business; and on this particular Monday morning, he awakes in a hotel room many miles from home. He has no idea that the Rapture had taken place around six o'clock; and when his alarm clock goes off at six-thirty, as usual, he gets up and turns on the TV. He always tunes in to the news each morning to check the stock market; but on this day, instead of the usual reports, he hears this shocking announcement: "Thousands of people disappeared from the Earth around six o'clock this morning! There has never been a tragedy of this magnitude to ever hit the world before. All the babies and young children are missing as well as many adults. The same reports are coming in from all over the world; it seems that no nation has been spared."

Barry stands shocked and speechless for the moment; but then he shakes himself a little thinking, "This is a strange sort of movie to be showing at this hour." He begins to flip from channel to channel, but every station has the same report. Barry's heart begins to pound so fast that he fears he might die of a heart attack as he cries out to himself, "This isn't possible; this can't be happening to our world!"

When he was a boy, he had been taught by his Sunday school teacher, Sadie Moore, about the signs of the second coming. "You must live holy, pure and clean," she would always say, "because one day, Jesus will come for His Bride. I've taught you the end-time scriptures, and you must realize that they're all being fulfilled in our day."

On this morning, Barry's thoughts go back to those teachings. Could it be that Sadie

Moore was right? Could the Bible she had loved and taught him and the other children about Sunday after Sunday be true? Is all that it said now being fulfilled?

Barry's mind is so overwhelmed and confused that it's like he's in a trance or moving in slow motion. At first, he can't seem to move at all because he's so weak from the shock of the news he has just heard. Finally, he manages to crawl to the telephone and call home; but he can't get through. Then he begins to whisper a prayer for the first time since he was a little boy, "Oh, God, if Sadie and my wife were right about your coming, help me to reach home and to hear from my wife and children." He calls several more times until he finally hears a ring on the other end. Oh, he can't wait to hear the sweet voice of his saintly wife answer; but as he waits, all he hears are the screams of people on the street below and a mother's shrill voice crying, "My baby is missing! Please, somebody help me!"

The telephone continues to ring, but no one answers. Then Barry takes a look from his third-floor hotel balcony at the scene below, and he senses his mind beginning to leave him as he witnesses nothing but madness and insanity. People seem to be running everywhere, and empty cars and trucks jam the street as far as he can see. He hears more voices crying out to God for help while others are screaming, "Come back, Jesus, come back! Don't leave me here!" Barry thinks that all of this must surely be a nightmare...little does he know that it's one from which he'll never wake up.

All Barry can think about is getting home to his wife and children; so he frantically calls the airport, but he can't get through. He starts to panic but then suddenly remembers a private plane charter company he has used in the past. He throws all of his things in his carry-on and rushes out of the room; but when he gets to the lobby, he realizes that he'll never be able to get a taxi. Even if he did, the driver wouldn't be able to go anywhere because the streets are filled with abandoned cars and trucks. In total desperation, Barry starts running down the street as fast as he can. The charter company's business office is at least twenty blocks away, but he knows this is the only way he'll get there.

When Barry finally arrives, he's as pale as paste; and he can hardly catch his breath. Barry has known the owner for quite some time; and he hopes the man will remember him on this crazy morning as he races into the office and without even waiting his turn blurts out, "It's me, Barry Gilmore, and I need to get onto one of your planes right away."

At first, the man doesn't recognize Barry; but after giving him a closer look, he says, "Yes, I remember you. Are you in a hurry to get somewhere?"

Barry quickly answers, "I can't get in touch with my wife or my children, and I have to get home right away."

"Well, I'm sure I can get you to a plane if you don't mind riding on my motorcycle to the airport; but because of all the insanity going on today, I don't know if I can get a pilot for you. I'll try my best; but in the meantime, you should settle down a little. Surely, you know that all of this is just a scare tactic. We've had these things before. Ever since the twin towers were destroyed in New York and so many died, the news media is forever trying to scare people into staying tuned to their reports."

Barry didn't bother to respond to the man other than to say, "Come on; let's get going." He just knows he has to get home. They both jump on the man's motorcycle; but when they finally arrive at the airport, there's nothing but total chaos. The man calls one of his pilots who says he doesn't think he can make it there but he'll try. All the roads remain jammed, and traffic is at a standstill.

While they're waiting, the owner fuels up one of the planes because he knows Barry is desperate. Then he starts the engine and lets it idle so that when the pilot arrives, they'll be ready to take off.

Barry can't stand still, and he paces up and down next to the plane. The pressure is almost more than he can take. Then he stops in mid-stride and turns toward the plane as he remembers that he has a small plane pilot's license. "What's wrong with me that I didn't think of that before?" he scolds himself.

So without another word to the owner, Barry jumps into the plane and taxies to the runway. He tries several times to contact the tower, but there is no response. He can see the owner of the charter service running after him shouting, "Stop, you fool! Stop!" So without wasting another minute, he taxies down the runway and takes off without even getting clearance from the tower; but Barry doesn't care. He's consumed with fear and has only one thing on his mind: "Are my wife and children really gone? Oh, God, no! Please, God, they can't have disappeared!"

Time seems to stand still up there in the sky, and Barry feels like he isn't even moving. Everywhere he looks, he seems to see images of Polly and his children; and he feels like he's about to lose his mind. When he begins to become more aware of his surroundings, it dawns on him that all planes must be grounded because he doesn't see another one the entire trip home. He calls the airport tower as he approaches the runway, but there's no answer; and after he lands, he discovers that there's not a soul to be found in the entire airport.

Barry leaves the plane in the middle of the runway, runs to his car and heads for home. He turns on the news only to hear a very haggard-sounding reporter repeating the same headlines: "Thousands have died because so many planes without pilots have literally fallen out of the sky and crashed all over the world. Trains have jumped the tracks everywhere, and thousands of abandoned cars and trucks have triggered mass car pileups all over the roads and highways. Never before has our nation experienced anything like this.

"My wife just rushed into the studio here to tell me that our little boy has disappeared, so I'm leaving here as soon as I sign off." The commentator chokes back tears, and Barry quickly turns off the news because he can't take any more.

Barry finally arrives home by winding his way through many little back roads; but his large, comfortable brick house appears to be so lonely, as if to say, "Everyone is gone from this home." Barry leaps out of his car and fumbles for his house key, but his fingers don't seem to want to work. When he finally gets the key in the door, he forces himself to stop and take a deep breath so he won't frighten the children; but as he turns the key in the lock, he wonders what he'll find behind that door. Will there be life? Will he hear the patter of little feet running and crying, "Mommy, Daddy's home?" But when he enters, all is as silent as a graveyard.

Barry runs in and out of every room screaming for the children and his wife, but they're gone. How could such a thing have happened? He runs into his bedroom and throws back the covers of Polly's bed, but only her lovely nightgown is lying there. She's gone, and she had left it behind. He stumbles into each child's room, and the scene is the same—their little pajamas are still in their beds, but they have all disappeared.

Barry falls down on his knees by one of his daughters' beds with tears pouring down his face as he cries, "Oh, my God, why didn't I go to church with my wife and babies? I could have been ready to go with my family!

Oh, Darling, you warned me again and again, but I didn't believe it could ever happen to me. Oh, God, have mercy! How can I live without my wife and children?"

Barry again tunes in to the news, and he has never witnessed such devastating scenes in his entire life. The whole world has been turned upside down. Hysterical people in every city under the sun are running around, searching for the missing Christians and for their loved ones.

In one news clip, a mother is seen clutching a tiny pair of shoes in one hand and her baby's clothes in the other and wailing at the top of her lungs, "One minute he was in my arms, and the next moment he was gone. There has to be an answer to this nightmare; it can't possibly be real!"

It's clear to Barry that the mother doesn't know the Bible as he listens to her continue, "I have tried to wake myself up from this nightmare, but I can't. I keep going into the nursery, but his little crib is empty; and only a teddy bear lies in his bed. Please help me! I think I'm losing my mind. I have called

9-1-1, but no one even answers. I've called the police, but I can't get through. My husband left for work early this morning, and I can't find him anywhere either. Help me, somebody! Please help me! I just have to find my baby!

"When he first disappeared, I ran across the street to my neighbor, Margo Sinclair. She's usually home at that time of the morning, but there was no sign of life. She's been such a wonderful neighbor who is always ready to help at any time; but when I pounded on her door, there was no answer. I tried ringing the doorbell and knocking louder, but there was still no answer. What's going on in this world?

"Only Saturday, I had talked to Margo; and she was so excited about the revival going on at her church that she had asked me to join her on Sunday to hear the evangelist preach on prophecy and the soon-coming of the Lord. That's never been my kind of thing; so I told her, 'Maybe some other time'; but now I don't know where she is.

"I had been in such a state of shock over

my little darling vanishing that until I walked out of the house, I hadn't seen all of the other people on my street running around looking for their children, too. I thought, 'What's going on here?' People all around me were screaming and crying as they raced up and down the street calling for their children. I thought I was losing my mind for sure; so I ran back into the house hoping to find that it was all just a bad nightmare, but that didn't happen. My baby is really gone!

"I quickly turned on the news, and I froze when I heard the word 'Rapture.' I had an old, fanatical granny who insisted on telling me over and over about Jesus coming for His Bride; but my mother never believed her, and she told me the story was just a bunch of nonsense. She said my granny had always talked about crazy things concerning God and His so-called Bride." The woman then looks at the news reporter and says, "Ben, since your TV station is close to my home, I managed to get here. Oh, please, for God's sake, help me find my baby! I can't live without my baby!"

As Barry continues to watch, Ben tries to move the woman off to the side and explain the situation saying, "Reports are coming in from all over the world that babies and little children are missing, and we're now receiving news reports that many adults have also disappeared. There has never been a time like this in the history of civilization. Pilots have disappeared and planes have literally fallen out of the sky. There are massive train, bus and subway accidents in cities around the world; and the roads are nothing but a disaster. I've never heard of or witnessed a worldwide tragedy that even comes close to this."

Barry stares in somber disbelief at the incomprehensible death and destruction, and many more heart-wrenching stories follow. Then just as Ben comments that there is yet no answer for the nightmare that started at six o'clock this morning, his sidekick, Chuck, excitedly rushes in claiming, "I have the answer. I found the explanation we've all been looking for right here in the Holy Bible. **Watch therefore: for ye know not what hour your Lord doth come** (Matthew 24:42)."

Chuck goes on to explain, "These are the words of Jesus Christ when He was here on Earth. He gave us all of the end-time signs in the twenty-fourth chapter of Matthew. It clearly describes this mysterious disaster and the fearful time we're now in. **This gospel of the kingdom shall be preached in all the world for a witness unto all nations; and then shall the end come** (Matthew 24:14). Jesus went on to say that the world has never seen anything like the time of Tribulation we're in and that unless the days are shortened, no flesh will be saved. **For then shall be great tribulation, such as was not since the beginning of the world to this time, no, nor ever shall be. And except those days should be shortened, there should no flesh be saved: but for the elect's sake those days shall be shortened** (Matthew 24:21,22)."

Chuck continues reading from God's Holy Book, "**But as the days of Noe were, so shall also the coming of the Son of man be. For as in the days that were before the flood they were eating and drinking, marrying and giving in marriage, until the day that**

Noe entered into the ark, And knew not until the flood came, and took them all away; so shall also the coming of the Son of man be. Then shall two be in the field; the one shall be taken, and the other left. Two women shall be grinding at the mill; the one shall be taken, and the other left. Watch therefore: for ye know not what hour your Lord doth come. Therefore be ye also ready: for in such an hour as ye think not the Son of man cometh (Matthew 24:37–42,44).

"For the Lord himself shall descend from heaven with a shout, with the voice of the archangel, and with the trump of God: and the dead in Christ shall rise first: Then we which are alive and remain shall be caught up together with them in the clouds, to meet the Lord in the air: and so shall we ever be with the Lord (I Thessalonians 4:16,17)."

Chuck holds up his Bible and declares, "All of this that has happened is true; God has spoken it. It's all laid out right here for those who will believe the Bible. I've been so foolish because I was taught the truth by my godly mom and dad, and I believed it until I went to college and had ungodly professors who taught me that the Bible was outdated and written by uneducated men who didn't know any better. Unfortunately, I listened to them and turned from God's truth and from His holy teachings; and now Jesus has come, and I'm left to face this Tribulation.

"This Bible I've been reading from belonged to my mom and dad. I stopped by their house on my way here to see if what they had taught me was really true. When I got there, my heart was beating like a hammer in my chest. Could it be possible that my mom and dad had been right all along? Would I find them missing? I held my breath as I entered the house; and as I had feared, there was only silence. I ran through the house where I'd had so many happy memories crying, 'Mom! Dad! Where are you?' Still, nothing but silence. Then I sensed a strange atmosphere in the house; and I just knew they were gone, caught away to be with the Lord. They had taught me throughout all my childhood days about the Rapture, and now it's happened. Oh, my God! It was all true; but the devil had used infidels and agnostic professors at my university to rob me of God's truth, and I allowed it.

"While I was at my parents' house, I'm not ashamed to admit that I fell down on my knees and cried out to God for the first time in many years. When I settled down enough to turn on the TV, I flipped to our station; and when I saw Ben, I immediately realized that my good partner didn't understand what had happened, and he needed answers."

Ben patted his friend Chuck on the back as he said, "Thank you, Chuck, for shedding some light on all of this. Now, I want to turn to a well-known minister from Alabesta, Dr. Morehead. He's the pastor of a large church there, and he also travels around the world preaching his doctrine.

"Dr. Morehead, thanks for being with us at a time like this. We're anxious to hear what you have to say about this tragedy."

Dr. Morehead arrogantly struts onto the screen as Ben reads a list of all of his various educational and theological degrees. His pompous air of superiority immediately turns Barry off; but he wants to hear what the man has to say, so he continues to listen. "I believe the Bible is a pretty good book," Dr. Morehead begins, "but it's definitely not infallible. It can no doubt help some people who need a crutch, but you certainly can't believe everything it says. It was written thousands of years ago, so it definitely can't be the final authority for people today."

Chuck interrupts Dr. Morehead and says, "I just read some scriptures from the Holy Bible that describe 'to a tee' what has happened here today—that Jesus came and took His Bride to Heaven. Since you don't seem to believe that, can you explain to our audience what actually has taken place and why people all over the world are missing?—all the babies and small children and many grownups as well?"

Dr. Morehead prides himself in having all the answers; so he says with a great deal of importance, "For years, religious cranks and fanatics have pulled all kinds of stunts trying to fool people about the coming of the Lord; and I have no doubt that they're behind this one, too. They most likely organized this plan in secret and told everyone involved to put it into action at six o'clock this morning. People who call themselves Christians have obviously hidden themselves away and kidnapped children to make it look like the Bible is telling the truth about Jesus' coming—that He has come as a thief in the night, stolen the so-called born-again people as well as all the babies and small children and taken them to Heaven. Mark my words—this will turn out to be the greatest act of deceit that the world has ever witnessed."

Chuck then interrupts Dr. Morehead again to ask, "Isn't it true, Doctor, that some people who were devout members of your church have left and joined Fairview Church in your same city because it taught the whole Word of God—that all the end-time signs in the Bible were being fulfilled and that the Rapture generation was now on planet Earth?"

"Oh, yes, some of our less-educated members did leave," he pompously replies. "They were very determined to hold up the Bible as being the infallible Word of God, so I was glad when they left. Since they didn't agree with my teachings, they would have poisoned others in my large congregation."

Chuck still can't find any truth in Dr. Morehead's comments, so he continues his questions. "Dr. Morehead, what are you going to tell your people in your upcoming services? Don't you realize that you won't be able to deceive them any longer and that many of them will hate you for teaching false doctrine and causing them to miss the one flight out?"

By this time, Chuck is getting under Dr. Morehead's skin; and he's a little annoyed when he replies, "I don't care what you say, Chuck. My people love me, and they believe whatever I tell them."

Ben cuts in to end the conversation by saying, "Well, Dr. Morehead, Please do come back in a few weeks and tell us how your church accepts what you tell them about what happened around six o'clock this morning."

Ben then turns to Chuck and says, "Stay on

with me if you can and answer some more of the people's questions. I sure can't explain any of this to all the hysterical mothers who are calling in about their missing children and begging for help. Some people are cursing God and blaming Him for this devastating catastrophe while others say that the Earth has been invaded by strange creatures that have abducted men, women and babies and have carried them away to other planets. Some even declare that they saw strange airships approaching and taking off from the Earth.

"There are also many people who recognize the fact that Jesus has come for His own just like the Bible said He would. Many people had a born-again grandmother or grandfather, uncle or aunt, or mom and dad who taught them the truth."

With a sincere sense of urgency, Chuck turns and directly addresses the viewers. "You need to find a Bible and start reading it right away. Everything that has happened today is in the Bible, and I do mean everything. You'll be amazed as you read the prophecies of years ago that have been and are being fulfilled, and today is a great fulfillment of prophecy.

"You've witnessed scene after scene of heartbroken and desperate people all over the world who are searching in vain for missing loved ones, but they won't believe the Bible. In some families, the mother and the little ones are missing, and the daddy is left; or the mother is left, and the daddy and children are gone. In others, both the mother and daddy are left; and the small children and babies are gone. The tormented, heart-wrenching screams heard all over the world are more than human minds could ever imagine. Many people have even left their jobs to join the great crowds who are searching for the missing Christians.

"Many of those Christians had warned for years of this terrible time, but too many people thought those Christians were just old-fashioned and different because they believed everything they read in the Bible was true. They thought Christians couldn't possibly be happy in this life while expecting Jesus to come and carry them away; and others thought they had plenty of time, that they would change their lives and live for Jesus one day.

"Many people have gone to church every Sunday, but it's been more of a social gathering than a spiritual gathering. The pastor doesn't really teach the Gospel of Jesus and seems to talk more about current events or sports. There are no Sunday night services that reach out for sinners like they used to and no altar calls. Many churches have even torn out their altars altogether.

"But there are others of us who have attended a church that was on fire for God. The altar is still there; people sought God in all the services, and the prophecies of the Bible came to light through the Holy Spirit. However, the godly, consecrated ones who were always warning the sinners and the lukewarm Christians to prepare for the Lord's coming are gone. Now, many are crying today, 'Oh, God, why didn't we get ready? We were told there was only one flight out, and now we're left to face the Tribulation Period.' Many people all over the world have rushed to the homes of devout ministers only to find them gone."

Barry remains glued to the TV, watching
one depressing story after another of misery
and destruction all over the world. When
he feels like he can't take another minute,
he jumps to his feet and races out the front
door toward the neighbor's house. He knows
the couple next door doesn't believe in the
coming of the Lord because he's discussed
it with them many times, but they have one
daughter, Dolly, who does believe; and she's
a lovely Christian girl who goes to the same
church that his wife, Polly, attended.

Dolly married a godly man, Edward Shoe-
maker, whom she met at Fairview. Dolly's
parents had tried to convince her not to marry
Edward because he was a devout Christian,
and they didn't like the fact that he believed
the whole Bible and lived it. They had tried
so hard to keep Dolly from marrying him, but
she had given her heart to the Lord; and there
was no way they could talk her out of it.

Barry rings the neighbor's doorbell, but
there's no response. He knocks hard, but
there's still no answer. Then he hears crying;

so he pounds on the door again, and it opens on its own. Having been close neighbors for a long time, he walks in; and he's amazed to find Jesse and Liz sitting on the floor in their living room with the Bible open in front of them. Jesse is attempting to read it to Liz, but she's sobbing so hard that she really isn't listening. By now, Barry's heart is nearly pounding out of his chest because he realizes that Jesse and Liz know the truth about the Rapture taking place.

In their overwhelming state of despair, they don't notice Barry walking in; but Jesse finally catches a glimpse of him and cries, "My God, Barry, it's happened! Our daughter was right; the Lord has come. She went to the revival meeting just last night while we watched the baby. Dolly was supposed to have picked up little Louise early this morning, but she never came. Dolly is always on time, so Liz tried to call her many times but could never get through.

"In the meantime, I decided to look in on Louise and was beside myself when she wasn't in her crib. I ran over and ripped off the blanket, and all that was there was her nightgown and her little doll. Oh, my God, Barry, our darling Louise is gone! I screamed for Liz to come quick; but all I could say was, 'She's gone! She's gone!'

"Liz had never seen me like that before; and she kept asking me, 'Jesse, what do you mean? What in the world is wrong with you?'

"Baby Louise has disappeared!" I cried. "I tried to call the police, but all the lines are busy."

In the middle of Jesse's horrible story, Liz bolts out the front door screaming for help. She runs into Susan King who looks so dazed and frightened herself that Liz hardly recognizes her. She's just wandering around the yard as one in a trance saying, "Please, help me find my little Henry. He's gone, and I can't find him anywhere." She seems to come to herself a little when she sees Liz; and she begins sobbing, "Liz, have you seen Henry? Somebody has stolen my little boy."

Liz looks up and down the familiar street, but everything appears painfully strange.

Neighbors have gathered in different yards—some are crying, some are screaming hysterically and others are praying out loud. Nicky from across the street is screaming, "Come back, Jesus, come back! Don't leave me!"

A little farther down the street, Liz hears Daisy desperately shouting, "Jesus, you took my precious husband, and I'm left. Have mercy on me! Oh, God, what am I going to do without him?" Liz knows that Daisy's husband was a devout Christian.

Liz takes off to join one group of neighbors whom she sees standing in the middle of the street. When she gets to them, she breaks down and bursts into tears; and as they stream down her cheeks, she sobs, "Our darling grandbaby, Louise, is missing." Everyone looks at her, but no one says a word. They all just stand there with fear stamped all over their faces.

This is too spooky for Liz, so she turns and runs back to the house where her husband is still searching the Bible for answers and telling Barry the story of Louise's disappearance over and over again. "Barry," Jesse pleads, "where is my daughter? I have to know if she's all right."

Barry finally says, "I'm sure your daughter and son-in-law have been raptured and that baby Louise was caught up with them. My wife and three children are also missing." As Barry begins to break down again, he manages to say, "Yes, the Rapture has taken place just like they tried to tell us it would; but we wouldn't listen or believe the Bible, and so we're left."

Barry, now blinded with tears, turns and stumbles out the door like a drunkard. "Oh, God," he sobs, "I wish I had never been born. I wish I could die. I can't live without my wife and babies." When he reaches home, he quickly closes the door, trying to shut out all the screams of the people.

CHAPTER
THREE

B arry Gilmore, Luther Calloway and Sidney Moore had been childhood buddies ever since they could remember. They grew really close and were the best of friends, even through high school. They all went to the same church; and Sidney's mother, Sadie Moore, was their Sunday school teacher. She was a very special person and a wonderful worker for the Lord who was always willing to help in the many activities of the church. She was so very kindhearted and filled with God's love that she became like a big sister to many of the young people. Each Sunday morning she would invite them to her house after service, and she became a great inspiration to them.

Sidney Moore and Luther Calloway grew up at Fairview Church, but Barry had come in later. His mother and dad were skeptics who did not believe the Bible was the infallible Word of God. They didn't want to hear Barry mention the salvation Jesus brought, God's prophecies or the soon return of the Lord. They scoffed and mocked at the very notion of people being raptured and changed in a moment and a twinkling of an eye.

Throughout his life, Barry had never heard his parents pray. They didn't like the fact that he went to church, but it kept him out of their hair on Sunday mornings. They liked to sleep in after a wild Saturday night out, so Barry would get up on his own and get himself ready to go to Sunday school and morning worship. His parents didn't seem to care what time he got home; so many times, Barry would have dinner with one of his buddies' families. He found great love in those families and always wished that he could have that same love in his home.

As time passed, the three boys graduated from high school and went away to college at different schools. Luther went to a Christian college and was blessed to be able to take some Bible classes in addition to those that were required for his major. One particular class that fascinated Luther was Bible prophecy. The professor who taught it was really knowledgeable in that subject, and Luther learned more than he had ever dreamed possible about prophecy. Later, Luther graduated from college and went back to his hometown where he became a good businessman; but with all he had learned about Bible prophecy, he was also able to teach a class on it at his church with great success.

Luther was a handsome man, six feet two inches tall with an athletic build, sandy blonde hair and blue eyes. He had a friendly, outgoing personality, an excellent voice for public speaking, and he was really dedicated and consecrated to God. He had a wonderful marriage with his childhood sweetheart, Bobbie, and they had a terrific set of twin boys who just added to their happiness. Things seemed to be going so well; but as time went on, Luther started to lose interest in teaching prophecy, and he finally gave up the class. Then he fell into a lukewarm state and began making excuses for missing church. His wife would warn him again and again about the end-time signs and the coming of the Lord, but Luther had allowed the devil to deceive him. He eventually began going out after work with the guys at his office and even started to do some social drinking. He kept promising his wife that he would soon go back to church on a regular basis; but on Rapture morning, he still had not gotten right with God.

On that life-changing Monday morning, Luther wakes up with a start; and he's puzzled to sense a heavy presence of the Lord in his bedroom. Could it be his imagination? He reaches over to wake Bobbie and ask if she also feels the presence of the Holy Spirit; but to his surprise, she's not there. He quickly sits up and notices that her covers look undisturbed. He knows something is going on because she never gets out of bed and leaves it like that. A nervous, fearful feeling begins to take him over as he jumps out of bed and hurries to the kitchen, but Bobbie isn't there either. Some mornings, he would find her sleeping with their four-and-a-half-year-old twins if one of them woke up sick or had a nightmare during the night; so he runs to their room to see if she's there.

When Luther enters the twins' bedroom, he feels the same strong presence of God in the room; and when he looks at their beds, the twins are gone. His fear grows more intense as he runs to the two little beds and throws back the covers only to find the boys' pajamas that they had been sleeping in still lying there. He stands staring at the sight in shocked disbelief, and he seems to be frozen in time as tormenting thoughts start flooding his mind. "Something awful has happened in this house," he mutters to himself. At that moment, the telephone rings; and it snaps him out of his stupor for the moment. When he answers, someone in a low, guarded voice asks, "Is that you, Luther? This is Barry. Do you know what happened this morning? I can't believe you're still here. I thought for sure you'd be gone, but you have been left, too!"

"What do you mean *left*?" Luther stammers.

"Haven't you heard the news this morning? My God, Luther, the Rapture took place around six o'clock this morning. People are missing all over the world, including my wife and my three beautiful girls. People are so beside themselves that they're losing their minds." Barry can't hold back the tears any longer as he cries, "Luther, what am I going to do without my family?"

Luther doesn't even bother to hang up. He just starts screaming as loud as he can and running like a wild man from room to room. "They can't be gone; they have to be here!" Luther feels the room start swimming around him, and he falls to the floor in a dead faint. When he finally comes to, he has no idea how long he's been on the floor or what happened to him; and he can't seem to get his bearings. Nothing around him appears to be real, and he lies there not having the strength to get up. Then the stark reality of what has happened begins to flood back into his mind, and scriptures flash before him as if they were lighted billboards. **For the Lord himself shall descend from heaven with a shout, with the voice of the archangel, and with the trump of God: and the dead in Christ shall rise first: Then we which are alive and remain shall be caught up together with them in the clouds, to meet the Lord in the air: and so shall we ever be with the Lord** (I Thessalonians 4:16,17). **For as in the days that were before the flood they were eating and drinking, marrying and giving in marriage, until the day that Noe entered into the ark, And knew not until the flood came, and took them all away; so shall also the coming of the Son of man be. Then shall two be in the field; the one shall be taken, and the other left. Two women shall be grinding at the mill; the one shall be taken, and the other left. Watch therefore: for ye know not what hour your Lord doth come** (Matthew 24:38–42).

The last verse almost makes his heart stop beating, and its words are now pounding in his brain like a sledgehammer. "Jesus has come, and I am left! Oh, God, what will happen to me now? I can't live without my precious wife and boys. When I taught prophecy, I often told my students, 'There's just one flight out. Be ready and don't miss it.' Now, because of my careless stupidity, I have missed that one flight out. Oh, dear God, I can't believe I'm actually in the Tribulation Period!"

After lying helpless on the floor for some time, Luther manages to get up and turn on the news. He watches with bated breath thinking it's all just a terrible nightmare, and he'll soon wake up. It's clear to him that some of the news commentators don't know the first thing about the Rapture or the Bible as they ignorantly try to put together all the pieces of what they're hearing but can't seem to make any sense out of it.

As Luther flips from station to station, the things he hears and sees are simply unbelievable. The entire world is consumed with stifling, naked fear and seems to have gone mad; many people have even lost their minds and committed suicide. Not one baby or small child can be found anywhere, and the frantic families of the missing are hopelessly searching and pleading for help.

Luther is stunned by one half-crazed news commentator on the verge of hysteria who literally shouts, "This is the worst calamity to ever strike the world. No nation has been spared. It's all a big mystery that we just can't seem to explain. Have countries actually been invaded? How and why have so many graves opened up, and who took all of the bones? All means of communication are jammed, and transportation is at a standstill. The agonizing cries of mothers and daddies frantically searching for their children pierce the air all over the world.

"Many callers who have gotten through on our news line are telling us to look in the Bible to find the answers we need, but how can they put so much trust in a Book that was written by men hundreds of years ago? By now, it has to be outdated and old-fashioned. I tell you, People, we can't depend on a book like that even if it is the Bible. The only answer that seems to make any sense regarding this great mystery is that the Earth has somehow been invaded by someone or something that has silently carried people away. Many have already vowed to never give up the search for their loved ones. They claim they can't really be gone and that they have to be somewhere."

As Luther continues watching, the story of the great prophet Elijah who went to Heaven comes to his mind. Elijah was raptured, but the sons of the prophets didn't believe it. They searched for Elijah for three days and nights even though Elisha—who had seen Elijah go to Heaven in a chariot of fire led by horses and had received Elijah's mantle of power—had told them not to go. **And it came to pass, as they** [Elijah and Elisha] **still went on, and talked, that, behold, there appeared a chariot of fire, and horses of fire, and parted them both asunder; and Elijah went up by a whirlwind into heaven. And Elisha saw it, and he cried, My father, my father, the chariot of Israel,** and the horsemen thereof. And he saw him no more: and he took hold of his own clothes, and rent them in two pieces. He took up also the mantle of Elijah that fell from him, and went back, and stood by the bank of Jordan; And he took the mantle of Elijah that fell from him, and smote the waters, and said, Where is the LORD God of Elijah? and when he also had smitten the waters, they parted hither and thither: and Elisha went over. And when the sons of the prophets which were to view at Jericho saw him, they said, The spirit of Elijah doth rest on Elisha. And they came to meet him, and bowed themselves to the ground before him. And they said unto him, Behold now, there be with thy servants fifty strong men; let them go, we pray thee, and seek thy master: lest peradventure the Spirit of the LORD hath taken him up, and cast him upon some mountain, or into some valley. And he said, Ye shall not send. And when they urged him till he was ashamed, he said, Send. They sent therefore fifty men; and they sought

three days, but found him not. And when they came again to him, (for he tarried at Jericho,) he said unto them, Did I not say unto you, Go not (II Kings 2:11–18)?

Luther had been taught the Bible nearly all of his life, so he knows there's no need to search for his wife and twins. They had been changed in a moment and a twinkling of an eye and caught away to be with the Lord forever. He knows he has failed God and been left. The Lord clearly said in His Bible that He would spew the lukewarm out of His mouth. **I know thy works, that thou art neither cold nor hot: I would thou wert cold or hot. So then because thou art lukewarm, and neither cold nor hot, I will spue thee out of my mouth** (Revelation 3:15,16).

Luther had already learned so much about the seven years of Tribulation, but he knows that he must now study the Bible like never before because the world has never seen anything like what they're about to see. Jesus said, **For then shall be great tribulation, such as was not since the beginning of the world to this time, no, nor ever** shall be. And except those days should be shortened, there should no flesh be saved** [on the face of the Earth]: **but for the elect's sake those days shall be shortened** (Matthew 24:21,22).

As the scriptures continue to flood his mind, Luther begins to think more clearly; but he's still weak and shaky. He gets his Bible and spreads it open on the carpet. Then he buries his face in its pages and weeps his heart out before God. He knows better than to blame God, and he's very aware that now he must pay the price for his failures.

Luther tries to reach Barry again, and the phone only rings once before Barry picks it up. "Barry, is that you?" Luther softly whispers. Barry can hardly make out the low voice, but he soon realizes it's Luther.

"Thank God it's you, Luther," Barry says somewhat relieved. "When we talked on the telephone not too long ago, you didn't even say goodbye or hang up; and I wondered what had happened to you. Luther, how could you, of all people, miss the Rapture? You know so much about Bible prophecy and the coming of Jesus."

"The sad, simple answer," Luther said, "is that I allowed myself to get into a lukewarm condition. I started going out with the wrong people, and I lost the anointing and vision of the Lord's coming. I allowed the devil to deceive me and convince me that Jesus wasn't coming for a long time, and now I'm left here while my wife and beautiful twin boys are gone! My wife warned me just this past Sunday evening that I needed to get back into church, and she reminded me that all of the end-time signs showed that Jesus would soon come. What a fool I was to let the devil put my mind in such a condition that I didn't listen to her. Barry, why don't you come over to my house. I'm sure it will help both of us to get together for a little bit."

Luther decides to step outside while he waits for Barry, but he soon regrets that decision. The agonizing cries of those with missing loved ones still pierce the air, and neighbors with tortured, swollen faces and bloodshot eyes begin to run over asking question after question: "Have you seen little Buddy?" "Do you know where my precious little daughter is?" "Can you help me find Jane?" "Could creatures from another planet really have taken my family away?" Others are just hopelessly crying, "My husband is missing." "My dear wife is gone." "Luther, please help us."

The whole neighborhood is such a pitiful sight that Luther feels he must give such tortured souls some kind of explanation. "Jesus has come," Luther begins, "and He's taken His saints to Heaven. All the babies and little children were still innocent, and that's why He took them, too. If you have a Bible, go home and read it. The answers are all in God's Holy Word."

Many of the people just stand there blankly staring at Luther, and he realizes he isn't getting anywhere with them. Whether they don't believe him or they just don't understand, it's clear to him that they aren't familiar with the Holy Scriptures like he is.

Luther soon becomes overwhelmed by all of this and seeks refuge back in the house; but once inside, he notices how cold and empty it feels. Oh, what a fool he has been! How could he have failed His wonderful Lord and Savior, Jesus Christ? He'd give anything right now if he could just live some of his life over. His mind is filled with all kinds of things he should have done differently and with horrifying thoughts of what's to come. He's never been in such a frightening situation in his whole life. People's names start to come to mind and he wonders, "Is he or she missing? Was she saved? Did he make the Rapture?"

Luther knows very well that many of the people who had attended Fairview Church are missing. He thinks of Sadie Moore and what an encouraging big sister she had been to him and to all of the young people at Fairview. He knows she's gone, but he feels compelled to try and call her just in case this is still a bad dream. After trying a number of times, he finally gets through; and someone does pick up the phone, but it's definitely not Sadie. Luther doesn't recognize the despondent and tearful voice; and he asks, "Who is this? Isn't this Sadie Moore's home?"

At first, there is nothing but dead silence.

Then the voice finally answers while trying to choke back the tears, "Yes, but she's gone." Then after a slight pause, the voice cries, "Did you hear me? My mother is missing!"

"Who is this?" Luther asks again.

"I'm Sadie's son, Sidney."

When he hears that, Luther almost faints; and he sits down in a chair to keep from falling over. "Sidney, this is Luther; you've missed the one flight out, too! Your mother told us so many times that Jesus was coming real soon. Surely you remember her always saying, 'Boys, be sure and be ready'; and then she would give us scriptures of prophecy to prove it. Your mother is missing, and my wife and twin boys are also gone."

Sidney just starts crying again and can't speak a word. When he finally stops, he manages to say, "My sweet wife and little boy are missing, too. Gabe was only five years old, and he was such a remarkable boy. He knew so many stories about Jesus, and he loved to walk around the house singing songs about Him. You already know how wonderful my mother was; but she was ready for the one

flight out, and she's in Heaven right now.

"Just yesterday evening, my wife begged me to go with her and little Gabe to the revival service at church. She told me how gifted the young preacher was in Bible prophecy and how he was making the coming of the Lord such living reality. She told me about all the souls who had come to the Lord during the revival; and just think, I could have been one of them. Then I would be with my boy, my wife and my mom today. Oh, Luther, my world has ended! Can I come over to your house for a while? I'm so miserable and afraid, and I don't know how I'll survive without my family."

"That's a great idea because Barry Gilmore is on his way here, too. I'm sure you remember him and all the great times the three of us had growing up together, and we always loved your mom. She was so sweet and a real blessing to us boys. She had plenty of the love of Jesus to share, and she taught us so much. Sidney, I have to go because someone's at my door. It's probably Barry, so hurry on over. It'll help all of us to be together."

Luther walks over to open the door; and as soon as he cracks it, Barry falls sobbing into his arms, his heart broken into many pieces. "Oh, Luther, how are we going to survive in this period of great Tribulation? The whole world has been turned upside down. My wife pleaded and pleaded with me to go to church with her and to live for the Lord. She was such a beautiful child of God; and I had promised her that when we got married, I would serve the Lord. She knew the difficult circumstances I faced in my family, and she gave me a chance; but I didn't keep my promise."

"Barry, since I talked to you on the telephone, I found out that Sidney Moore was also left. His wife, son and mother are missing; so he asked if he could come over, too. He really needs to be with us, and we all need each other's support. He should be here any time."

Just then, there's a knock at the door; and sure enough, it's Sidney. Instead of walking in, Sidney just falls to the floor sobbing uncontrollably. Luther pats him on the back and helps him get up. The three of them just sit silently for a while, staring at each other and fighting the storm of turmoil going on inside. Their worlds have ended, and all those they have ever held dear are gone. All three are overwhelmed with shame and regret at being left because they had known the light of the truth and that the Bible foretold the coming of the Lord...but they didn't think it would happen so soon.

The three boys finally start to talk a little, and then they decide to go to Fairview Church. When they arrive, they find the church completely filled with frightened, tortured people who are all crying their hearts out. After sitting there for just a short while, Barry and Sidney are amazed to see Luther get up without a word and walk to the platform. Many people know Luther, so everyone instantly gets deathly still. They can't believe Luther was left, and they wonder what he will say. Barry overhears someone telling a reporter who Luther is and how knowledgeable he is in Bible prophecy.

With a trembling hand, Luther reaches out

and takes the microphone. His voice is very low and broken at first, but it gets a little stronger as he gains more control of himself. "To our Lord's shame and our own," Luther begins, "we have been left. I know many of your family members are missing, and my dear wife and twin boys are gone, too." People begin weeping aloud, and Luther pauses as he wipes the tears from his eyes. Then he manages to continue, "I know the Holy Scriptures, and I know exactly what's taken place. I'm so ashamed to stand before you this day and tell you that I have failed my God, my family and myself."

Luther pulls his New Testament out of his pocket and begins to read, "**But I would not have you to be ignorant, brethren, concerning them which are asleep, that ye sorrow not, even as others which have no hope. For if we believe that Jesus died and rose again, even so them also which sleep in Jesus will God bring with him. For this we say unto you by the word of the Lord, that we which are alive and remain unto the coming of the Lord shall not prevent**

them which are asleep. For the Lord himself shall descend from heaven with a shout, with the voice of the archangel, and with the trump of God: and the dead in Christ shall rise first: Then we which are alive and remain shall be caught up together with them in the clouds, to meet the Lord in the air: and so shall we ever be with the Lord. Wherefore comfort one another with these words (I Thessalonians 4:13–18).

"Those who were ready have been caught up to meet the Lord in the air. I was taught the Holy Scriptures as a child, and I grew up knowing about the prophecies of the second appearance of Jesus and His plan to take His Bride to Heaven. Jesus warned us, **Therefore be ye also ready: for in such an hour as ye think not the Son of man cometh** (Matthew 24:44). He also said through John the Revelator, **If therefore thou shalt not watch**, **I will come on thee as a thief, and thou shalt not know what hour I will come upon thee** (Revelation 3:3).

"Our Lord did come as a thief, and none of

us were watching. I confess that I used to be watching and was a devout student of God's infallible Word, but I reached out for the ways of the world. I knew better, so there's no excuse for me today. Jesus told us what end-time signs we should look for just before He would return. We saw the signs daily but failed to heed them just as the people did before the Flood in Noah's day. God warned those people, too, but they didn't heed the call of God and were left outside the ark when the Flood came.

"We are now in the great Tribulation Period that the Bible told us would come; but, thank God, we have another opportunity to yield to Him and know that He still loves us. We all need to come to this altar and pray through to Heaven's victory just like many have done before us. Then we'll be able to meet our loved ones in Heaven one day. God's mercy is still here, and the Lord loves each one of us."

People all over the building begin moving toward the altar at once and pouring their hearts out to God, "Lord, have mercy upon our souls. Oh, God, please forgive us!" Desperate cries of great sorrow and humility have filled the house of God.

The three boys stay and pray for some time, not only for themselves but for others. When they finally get up to leave, they're concerned about three girls whom they saw there—Violet, Sally and Purple Belle. They all looked so tortured and alone, and the boys' hearts were bleeding for them.

Purple Belle had been through a great tragedy when she was just three years old—both of her parents were killed in an automobile accident. However, she was very fortunate to have loving grandparents who took her in and raised her as their own.

Purple's granddad particularly adored her, and he's the one who had affectionately nicknamed her Purple because she loved the color purple so much. She wanted all of her clothes to be purple; and when she was little, she even dressed all of her dolls in purple. Others picked up on the nickname, so she grew up being known as Purple Belle. Unfortunately, Purple had not shown her grandparents the love, kindness and appreciation she should have; and she was a very disobedient child.

Sally, or Sal as many people called her, was an unruly child as well. She was hard to control at home, in church and everywhere else; and she wouldn't listen to anyone. She always wanted to do her own thing; and now, she is going to have to pay dearly for it. The mother and dad she so horribly disrespected and mistreated are missing; and as the three boys talk, they're quite sure she's going through hell over the way she treated her parents.

The third girl, Violet, had always been a good, moral girl; and the boys can't remember ever hearing anything bad out of her. They really thought she was saved, and they're amazed to have seen her and to know that she missed the Rapture. They feel so sorry for her because they knew the rest of her family well, and they know for sure that they're all missing. Oh, what she must be going through!

As the boys walk home from Fairview, they start knocking on different doors to check on people they know. They're sure that Mother Collins is gone; but they stop to knock on her door anyway, and they actually hear somebody coming. When the door opens, they see that it's Jim, her son. He breaks down and begins to cry his heart out, and they try their best to hug and console him. "My baby, Sue, was raptured," he says between sobs. "Mom is gone, too; and my wife, Lucille, is acting like she's about to lose her mind. I can't do anything with her; she just screams nonstop, 'I want my baby! My baby has been kidnapped!' She won't accept the fact that the Lord has come because she was raised in a home of infidelity and taught there was no God."

Jim never should have married Lucille, but he did. He thought he could change her; but instead, she changed him and persuaded him to stay out of church. Lucille didn't even like Mother Collins to take her own granddaughter to Sunday school, but she would allow her to once in a while just to keep the peace. Now, baby Sue is gone, and she'll never become a victim of the devil's infidelity because she's safe in the arms of Jesus.

The boys hear so many sad stories and encounter so many unfortunate situations as they continue on their way. It's tearing their hearts out to meet people they have known for years and to see that they have been left behind.

As they turn onto another street, the three boys stop at John Coe's small house on the corner. Luther knocks on the screen door, but there's no answer. He tries the front door and finds it unlocked, so he slowly opens the door and calls out John's name. Still, there's no answer, so the boys decide to follow Luther inside. When they get to the kitchen, they find a handwritten note lying on the table which says, "My loved ones have been raptured, but I have been a miserable failure. I wasn't ready for the one flight out, and I can't stand to live another moment in this world. Goodbye."

The boys feel a cold, eerie presence in the house as they look at each other in bewilderment. Luther feels as if he's walking into a dense curtain of fear and utter despair, fear so real that it's like a thick fog you could cut with a knife. They can all tell that something is seriously wrong here. As they continue searching, they receive the shock of their lives when they see the lifeless body of John Coe hanging from the upstairs banister, his eyes bulging from their sockets. Poor John had hung himself and sent his soul to hell. All three are sobbing aloud now, and the wall of fear feels so real and penetrating that they rush from the house without even cutting the body down. They run down the street like legions of devils are after them. They want to get as far away from the sight as possible, but it's one they'll never be able to forget.

The boys eventually slow down to catch their breath, and they walk along saying nothing for quite a while. Finally, they muster enough courage to knock on another door, but they don't realize whose house it is until Purple Belle comes to the door. When she first sees them, she throws herself into their arms, crying uncontrollably. They finally get her calmed down so they can talk to her; and in between sobs, she tells them that her grandparents are missing. Then she confesses to them, "I thought at times that I really hated them, but I know now that I didn't. I would give anything if I could just have them back right now."

Purple continues pouring her heart out saying, "I realize the devil deceived me because I went around with the wrong crowd. It was like a nightmare when I first discovered my grandparents were missing and that the one flight out had taken place. Deep down in my heart, I had intended to get right with God one day. I always thought my grandparents were old-fashioned and weren't treating me right, but now I realize that they sacrificed their very lives to try to give me everything I wanted. What am I going to do without them? God have mercy on my soul!"

The boys try to comfort Purple Belle the best they can, and they encourage her to really seek God and pray so she can still go to Heaven. However, she just can't seem to believe that God will forgive her for how cruel she was to her grandparents. The boys leave Purple Belle in tears, praying that she will soon be able to yield to the Lord.

As the boys continue on down the street, they decide to stop in the cemetery to see if graves had really opened; and they're shocked to see that so many have. There are people everywhere trying to take in the unbelievable sight. The resurrection of the righteous had definitely taken place, and they can clearly see the evidence all over the big cemetery. People sit next to empty graves crying and praying—some are begging for Jesus to come back while others don't understand and are wondering why and how someone could have stolen the bodies of their loved ones. Unfortunately, some of them will never understand the truth because they won't accept the Holy Word of God.

The boys see more heartbreaking sights than they ever imagined, so they decide to leave; they have seen enough sorrow and heartache. On their way out, Luther speaks up to say, "We must stay as calm as we can no matter what goes on around us. We must devote ourselves to living in the Word of God, praying and fasting because we must have the help of God in this final hour." Barry and Sidney agree, and then they go their separate ways. It's getting late.

The next day, Luther calls Barry and suggests, "Let's go to Dr. Morehead's church and see what he has to say about all of this. I saw on the news this morning that there's been a lot of trouble there because different members are blasting him for all his deceit and blaming him for causing them to miss the one flight out."

Barry and Luther meet at the church a short time later; and when they enter the sanctuary, they're surprised to see one of the church deacons handing Dr. Morehead a beautifully wrapped gift because they'd heard that the old deacon, Brother Spencer, was against Morehead. The two of them have had a lot of trouble in the past; and for many years, Morehead hasn't wanted anything to do with Brother Spencer. The congregation sits quietly as everyone waits to see what's inside.

The deacon turns to go back to his seat while Dr. Morehead stands there with tears in his eyes and says, "Brother Spencer, you and I haven't seen eye-to-eye on most things, so I'm very touched that on a morning like this you would be so thoughtful as to bring me a gift." The old deacon doesn't answer but just nods and waits for Dr. Morehead to open the package. When he finally unwraps it, the minister looks at the gift in astonishment and says, "Brother Spencer, there must be some mistake. You evidently intended to give me a Bible, but all that's here is a front and back cover."

Brother Spencer very calmly stands and says, "That's no mistake, Pastor. Down through these many years, every time you told us in your sermons that we didn't need this verse or that verse for today, I went home and tore it out of my Bible. This morning, I found that all I had left was the cover; so I thought it would be very appropriate to give it to you."

For years, Dr. Morehead had claimed to preach the truth from a holy pulpit; but Brother Spencer knew all too well that he had never served the true Word of God.

Most of the people begin to leave, but a few stay because they're not finished with

Dr. Morehead yet. One woman speaks up and says, "The God of Heaven tells us in the book of Revelation that if you take anything from His Bible, He will take your name out of His book of life." **And if any man shall take away from the words of the book of this prophecy, God shall take away his part out of the book of life, and out of the holy city, and from the things which are written in this book** (Revelation 22:19). "Since you have taken so much out of God's Word, He has taken your name out of His book of life, Dr. Morehead.

"You had a wonderful mother," she continues, "who taught you the Bible truth in your childhood. She used to come here to your church, but you were ashamed of your own mother. I remember one Sunday morning when she stood up to testify of God's love and promises, but you told her to sit down because she was out of order. You broke your own precious mother's heart, and she walked out of this church and never came back. Thank God she went to Fairview to hear the truth, and she's in Heaven today. God saw to it that she left you and your dead church behind, and it's good that she did."

Other church members then begin to rise up with hate for his deceit pouring out of their mouths. One person cries, "We're never coming back here again. You have destroyed our lives, but you're not going to destroy our souls. We're going to Fairview to be with those who want the truth!"

At that point, many of those in the congregation leave to go to Fairview; and when they arrive, they find it nearly filled but quiet. The congregation is drinking in every word the speaker is saying, and those who have just arrived are amazed.

All that's happened over the past day and a half isn't a mystery to this speaker. He knows the truth but is in deep sorrow to have missed the one flight out. "Our pastor here at Fairview always told us the truth," the speaker says. "He taught us the end-time signs from the Bible and declared over and over that we were the Rapture generation. How often I heard him say, 'Children, the Bible tells us to examine ourselves.' **Examine yourselves,**

whether ye be in the faith; prove your own selves (II Corinthians 13:5). He told us that Jesus was coming for those who were watching. **Blessed are those servants, whom the lord when he cometh shall find watching: verily I say unto you, that he shall gird himself, and make them to sit down to meat, and will come forth and serve them** (Luke 12:37)."

Mrs. Worthington, a longtime member of Dr. Morehead's church, doesn't leave with the others because she still has many things she wants to say to Dr. Morehead on this morning. A devoted member no more, she stands up against Dr. Morehead and tells him that he should be ashamed of preaching false doctrine to them down through the years. "You're an arch deceiver," she cries, "and we despise you for what you have done to us. Your deceit has brought us defeat. You're a preacher of the world church, not the Jesus Church; and we now see you for who you really are—a pompous, old fool!"

Another man jumps right up in agreement and says, "I've attended this church

and listened to your lies for fifteen years."
Someone else immediately chimes in, "Yes,
you even told us many lies about Fairview
Church and its pastor; but I just came from
there, and that pastor was raptured. Many
people who left this church over the years
and went to Fairview were also on the one
flight out because they made the right choice.
I've talked with some of our members since
yesterday morning who wish they had never
met you because you caused them to miss
the Rapture, and they're waiting for God to
destroy you. God says in His Holy Bible,
**Vengeance is mine; I will repay, saith the
Lord** (Romans 12:19)."

Luther and Barry have heard enough of Dr.
Morehead as well, and they hurry out of that
dead church. When they get back to Luther's
house, he turns on the TV just in time to hear
the newscaster making a big announcement:
"Tomorrow morning at nine o'clock, the great
so-called superman will introduce himself
and speak to the world. He claims to have
all the answers we need for this world crisis
because we have recently learned that many

more people are missing than was originally reported. The count is now well into the millions. Again, tune in tomorrow morning at nine to hear this great man."

Luther never thought he'd actually see the real Antichrist because he always thought he'd get right with God before it was too late; but now, he's about to see that devil-man. Luther and Barry immediately call Sidney to see if he has heard the announcement, and then they all decide to meet at Luther's house to watch the so-called superman's message together.

On Wednesday morning, all three boys gather around the screen just as the announcer says, "Stay tuned; the world's so-called superman is up next." After a brief advertisement, there is the devil's own man right on the screen. "Ladies and Gentlemen, I am the savior of the world, the true messiah the Jewish nation has been anticipating for thousands of years. I am the real Christ." As the Antichrist speaks, the three boys have to hold on to their chairs to keep from falling down on the floor in front of the TV and honoring the so-called superman. They're astounded at the power he has over them. They know that he is definitely the little horn Daniel wrote about. **I considered the horns, and, behold, there came up among them another little horn...and, behold, in this horn were eyes like the eyes of man, and a mouth speaking great things** (Daniel 7:8).

"I have all the answers we need to get us through this disaster," he continues. "I have come from Heaven to be your savior and to bring you all safely out of this world crisis. No one else can bring you out but me. I promise you that I will work hard and will join hands with the world church to bring about a peaceful end so we can all have perfect unity. I have the supernatural powers that the world church has been promising people for a long time, and I will use them to bring all the nations of the world together. I will bring peace, not turmoil; and I welcome each one of you listening to the sound of my voice to check my work daily. You will soon have perfect assurance that I am all that I claim to be.

"Today, I will make a covenant with the Jewish nation for seven years. They have been so misunderstood and mistreated for so long; but I am here to be their real savior at last, the lord and christ whom they have been expecting to come."

Luther turns to the other two boys and solemnly says, "Yes, Daniel's little horn has arrived." Luther has so much knowledge of prophecy, and he encourages Barry and Sidney to read about the little horn in the book of Daniel. "It will help you to understand the false superman," he explains. "You will hear him make glowing promises and covenants, but the great prophet Daniel uncovers him in God's Holy Word as the arch deceiver."

Luther knows that the first three-and-a-half years will be ones of false peace. He knows that when people begin to accept the Antichrist's peace, the Bible says there will be sudden destruction. **For when they shall say, Peace and safety; then sudden destruction cometh upon them, as travail upon a woman with child; and they shall not escape** (I Thessalonians 5:3).

The superman continues talking, "I will make a seven-year covenant with the Jews this day, and I will also make a covenant with the world church. They're going to rule along with me, and I promise you that things will be different; you'll see."

Once the announcement is over, Luther says, "Boys, things will get much worse when, after the first three-and-a-half years, you have to decide whether or not to take the Mark of the Beast. You won't be able to buy anything or even get your money out of the bank without it. Terrible times are coming, times like the world has never seen before; but the Bible tells us all about them. We must prepare and be ready, and God is the only one who can help us do that; so we must yield to Him continually every day."

CHAPTER
FOUR

In the huge crowd gathered at Fairview Church the day the Rapture had taken place sit three young girls who have grown up in the church—Violet Williams, Sally Morgan and Purple Belle. The three girls are not blinded by the devil's darkness; they know the truth, and they know that the true saints of God have been changed in a moment, in a twinkling of an eye and caught away to be with the Lord in Heaven forever. Oh, if only they had been ready!

As with many of the others there today, they had been warned again and again; but they had been careless and allowed the devil to deceive them into believing that the coming of the Lord would not be soon and probably not even in their lifetime. Oh, they knew the Bible was pure truth, but they thought the preachers and Sunday school teachers were just a little off on the timing of His coming. They were young, and they figured they would serve God with their whole hearts when they got older...but how wrong they were.

Before the Rapture, the three girls had been attending most of the services at their church. In fact, Violet had been there just this past Sunday night when the young evangelist had made the coming of the Lord so very real. She had almost gone to the altar but changed her mind at the last minute. Sally and Purple Belle were not there that night because they had gone somewhere else to have what they called a good time.

Purple Belle had gone to a wild party filled with drugs, alcohol, rock music, dancing and the works. Although her grandparents had raised her in church and taken her to Sunday school every weekend, she no longer listened to them. She didn't have a very sweet or gracious personality; she would pout when she didn't get her way and lie to get around her grandparents. She was very rebellious in high school and caused a lot of trouble there and at home. She would go to the altar at times to ease her conscience, but she never became really consecrated to the Lord. She loved to hang out with the kids at school more than she did those at church, and she wanted God on her own terms.

Purple's grandparents had sacrificed their lives for her; and they often went without so she could have the many things she wanted. They gave her nothing but love and kindness, but she never appreciated what they did for her.

Purple's granddaddy had a very special love and adoration for her, and he would try to talk to her about her ways when she was in high school. He knew she was hanging out with the wrong crowd and doing the wrong things, and he would warn her again and again; but she didn't pay any attention to him, and now she was left behind.

As Purple Belle sits in church this dreadful morning, the Bible teachings she has received roll over and over in her mind like mighty ocean waves. What a fool she has been! She had stayed out late the night before and had come home high on drugs; but her grandparents were in bed, so they didn't know when she came in. She's in her senior year of high school, and it's exam time. She knew she hadn't been studying like she should and that she would probably flunk the exams, but her grandparents would never allow her to miss school. So in a drug-induced stupor, she fell into a troubled sleep, not realizing that in a few short hours the one flight out would take place.

Purple Belle had awakened at about eight o'clock this morning; and when she had looked at the clock, she couldn't believe her eyes. Her grandparents had always called her in plenty of time for school, so why hadn't they gotten her up? She angrily jumped out of bed and went to find them. She stomped through the house calling for them, but there was no answer. She finally went into their bedroom, and that's when she knew something was really wrong. She noticed that the covers were not thrown back, and she could tell right away that they weren't there. She runs over and rips back the covers to find only their sleeping clothes there...but they are both gone.

For the first time, she began to sense a strange, heavy presence in the room; and instantly, the word "Rapture" flashed before her. She immediately froze, and fear gripped her body like a vise. Her mind screamed, "It's not possible; they can't be gone! This has to be a nightmare, and I'll wake up real soon. It must just be the effects of the drugs and alcohol from last night."

Purple Belle finally made it to the living room; and in a daze, she sank down in a chair. She picked up the remote and turned on the television without even thinking about what she was doing; and the first thing she heard was, "This is a special report—thousands of people disappeared from the face of the Earth about six o'clock this morning." A death-like chill took her over, and all the life seemed to drain from her body. Her mind began spinning with a whirlwind of horrifying thoughts; and she began to sob, "It can't be! It just can't be!"

The news reporter continued as he choked back his tears, "All the babies and little children are missing, and many adults are missing, too. It's the worst tragedy to strike the world in the history of mankind, and the same reports are flooding in from all over the world. It's a dumbfounding, worldwide mystery that we don't yet have any answers for."

Purple Belle sat there not knowing what to do and wondering what would happen to her now. The only two people who had really loved her were gone. There was no need to look for them because she knew they had gone with Jesus in the Rapture. Then she started to think about her friend Sal Morgan. She knew Sal was not ready to make the Rapture, so she tried to call her. After several tries, she finally got through; but then a voice she didn't recognize answered.

"Is that you, Sal?" Purple tentatively asked.

"Yeah, it's me," a voice very unlike Sal's stammered.

"Sal, this is Purple."

"My God," Sal cried, "you missed the one flight out, too!"

"Yes, and my grandparents are gone."

"My parents are gone, too," Sal cried. "Purple, what's going to happen to us? What are we going to do? I've been calling people all morning who go to Fairview, but I haven't been able to reach hardly any of them."

"Oh, Sal, we must help each other. Can you meet me at Fairview Church in half an hour?"

"Yes, I'll be there. I don't like hanging around this house with my parents gone."

Purple Belle hung up thinking, "I'm in such a state; how am I ever going to get dressed? I can hardly seem to move, but I must get to Fairview. I have to get up from here and get ready." As the tears rolled down her cheeks, she kept saying to herself, "What a fool I have been. Oh, Jesus, please forgive me!"

Somehow, Purple Belle finally got dressed. Then she just wandered aimlessly around the house saying, "Oh, Grandmother and Grand-dad, you were so good to me. You taught me God's truth, and I'm so sorry I didn't listen." All they had taught her seemed to be pounding in her brain, and it felt like her heart was beating out of her chest.

When she first got to the church, Purple Belle saw Sal standing outside still crying, her face puffy and her eyes swollen. They fell into each other's arms, sobbing loudly and clinging to each other as if for dear life. They finally tore themselves apart and decided to go inside the church. They found seats at the back; and when they looked around, they were amazed to see Violet Williams sitting by herself and weeping softly. They carefully made their way over to her, and then all three of them burst into tears. They had never felt such loneliness and grief.

Now, the three girls just sit there looking around with tear-dimmed eyes. They've cried so much that they don't have the strength to cry even one more tear. They feel their lives are over and that there's nothing left to live for. Even the church they love so much is gone because, although the building still stands, all the true saints who had made Fairview different from most other churches are missing. They do see some people they know in the audience, but most of the others they have never seen at Fairview before.

As they continue to sit there feeling so alone, they're shocked to look up and see Luther walk in with Barry and Sidney. They're aware that at one time, Luther had taught prophecy and been a devout worker in the church; but they also remember that he hasn't been to church for some time now.

As soon as Luther walks in, someone asks him to please explain to the crowd what has happened. Of course, Luther agrees because he now wants to bring as many souls to the Lord as he possibly can. He begins to speak, and the three girls hang on every word as Luther explains the Rapture in such biblical simplicity. When Luther finishes, the crowd seems to move as one person for the altar; and no longer does anyone seem to be ashamed to cry out to God for mercy.

When the girls stop praying, they notice that

Luther, Barry and Sidney have left. They go back to their seats and sit down because the church seems to be their only refuge from the now frightening world. They feel so abandoned and scared. The girls had grown up looking into the many loving faces of the true saints of God, but now they're all gone.

Sally sits there completely sober-minded for a change and trying to figure out why she let the devil deceive her so badly. In her mind, she relives how arrogant and rebellious she's been and how she didn't want to be told what to do. She wouldn't listen to the pastor or her parents, but now she realizes just how wonderful her mother and dad had really been and how much they had loved her in spite of all she had done. She had sassed them, made many hurtful remarks and done many sinful things when she was out of their sight; and at the time, she didn't even care. She had run around with the wrong crowd and tried to do all the "in things" no matter how much of the truth she had been taught. She got to the point where she actually thought she hated her mother and dad when really she was just ashamed of what they believed. She longs to tell them how sorry she is, but they're no longer with her today.

"Oh, Lord," Sally confesses, "I've been so awful to my parents, and I've spit in your dear eye many times. I'm so sorry. If only I had my mom and dad with me today, I would give them the love and honor they deserve. Oh, dear Jesus, do help me. I wish the pastor was here so I could ask his forgiveness for the terrible spirit I showed in church and for the times I disturbed the services. The ushers were always after me, telling me to be quiet; but the devil caused me to just laugh at them. I'm so sorry for the mess I've made of my life, especially when I've had the truth all along; and I could have been on the one flight out."

Violet sits beside Sally very quiet and still as she always did when she was in church. She had a precious, godly mom and dad and one older sister who had served the Lord from the time she was a child. Violet is different from Purple and Sally in that she always respected God and the church, and she never caused any trouble. She's always been a good, moral person but has never been truly born again. She had planned to live for the Lord Jesus some day, but she thought she had plenty of time. She never could really believe that the Lord was coming soon, and she thought it probably wouldn't happen in her day.

Just last night, Violet had been in the revival service; but she'd fought off conviction. She knew that she needed to go to the altar, but she didn't. If only she had known it would be her last call before Jesus would come for His own. She thought of the scripture, **Therefore be ye also ready: for in such an hour as ye think not the Son of man cometh** (Matthew 24:44).

Violet's sister, Myrtle, had been sleeping by her side when she went to bed Sunday night; but when she woke up this morning at seven o'clock and reached over to wake her up, Myrtle wasn't there. Violet knew that was odd because Myrtle didn't usually get up first. Violet looked across the room and noticed that Myrtle's covers weren't disturbed. Then she jumped out of bed and threw back the covers on Myrtle's side to find only her nightgown there. Everything was so strange, and Violet wondered what was going on.

She started running through the house, expecting to find Myrtle at any time; but she was nowhere to be found. Even stranger was the fact that her mom and dad weren't there either. Violet knew that Mom was always in the kitchen at that time of the morning, but not today. Then Violet began to notice an unusual atmosphere in the house. Even the smell of the air was strange, and she couldn't figure it out.

At that moment, Violet heard the next-door neighbor screaming, "Somebody, help me! My baby has disappeared!" Immediately, panic seized Violet; and as she started to run toward the front door, it suddenly felt as if she was running in slow motion. Her feet felt like lead, and she could hardly pick up one foot after the other. She somehow managed to get to the front door and open it; and she saw Mrs. Foretell in her front yard screaming hysterically, "My baby! Someone has kidnapped my baby!" It was too much for

Violet to take, and she fell to the ground in a dead faint.

When Violet came to, another neighbor from across the street, Mrs. Winslow, was wiping her face with a wet cloth. "What happened?" Violet asked in amazement.

"Honey, you fainted," Mrs. Winslow answered. "Here, let me help you into the house."

"Did you hear about Mrs. Fortell's baby disappearing?" Violet anxiously asked.

"Oh, Honey, haven't you listened to the news this morning?" Mrs. Winslow responded. "The whole world is in an uproar. Babies and little children are missing in every country, and even multitudes of adults are gone. According to the news reports, it's the most tragic, puzzling and widespread mystery the Earth has ever seen. Some people declare that the Rapture took place about six o'clock this morning. I had never put much thought into what some called the Rapture, but this startling news has changed my mind. I really think I need to spend some time studying my Bible."

All the color instantly drained from Violet's face as she slowly whispered, "I haven't had the news on this morning; but when I woke up, my sister Myrtle wasn't in bed like she usually is, and I couldn't find my mom and dad. I've searched everywhere, but I can't find them. Oh, my God, Mrs. Winslow, they're gone! All three of them believed in the Rapture of the saints of God; they lived holy before the Lord and were expecting Him to come. I haven't been serving the Lord like I should, and now the Lord has come just like the Bible said He would. His holy people have been changed in a moment and in a twinkling of an eye, caught away to be with Him forever."

With that realization, beads of cold sweat popped out on Violet's forehead; and she started shaking all over as thousands of thoughts flooded her mind. "How could this have happened to her? It has to be a nightmare. The one flight out couldn't possibly have taken place." But as Violet slowly closed her eyes in bitter remorse, she knew she had missed the Rapture. When she opened her eyes again, Mrs. Winslow was gone.

Violet finally got up and turned on the news, and she stood speechless watching and listening to the unbelievable chaos taking place all over the world. The reporter was grimly stating, "The whole world has gone stark-raving mad. We're hearing from every nation that all the babies are gone. I have never believed in the Bible; but since so many people have called in today and told me to get a Bible and learn the truth, I think it's time for all of us to check it out. Many claim that Jesus came and took His people to Heaven."

The reporter turned and asked a lady with a Bible to join him, and she began to read scripture after scripture about the Rapture and how people would be changed in a moment. "**Behold, I shew you a mystery; We shall not all sleep, but we shall all be changed, In a moment, in the twinkling of an eye, at the last trump: for the trumpet shall sound, and the dead shall be raised incorruptible, and we shall be changed** (I Corinthians 15:51,52)." Violet didn't think she could take much more, and she switched off the TV.

All of these things are going over and over in Violet's head as she sits there in the congregation at Fairview, and she doesn't have a doubt about the Rapture. She knows the scriptures, and she knows they're all true. How she rebukes herself for letting the devil deceive her as she whispers under breath, "I know I'm in the great Tribulation the Bible tells us of and that the Antichrist will reveal himself and make a covenant with the Jews for seven years. I know the hour will come when I can't buy or sell unless I take the Mark of the Beast—666. Please, God, I plead for you to have mercy on me! Give me strength as only you can do so that I will never take the Mark of doom. I know, God, that if I take the Mark, I will have to sell my soul to the devil; and I could never again get right with you. I will have blasphemed against the Holy Ghost, and Jesus said there is no forgiveness for that now or for all eternity." **But he that shall blaspheme against the Holy Ghost hath never forgiveness, but is in danger of eternal damnation** (Mark 3:29).

When Violet gets home from Fairview, she falls on her knees and prays and cries before the Lord for hours. She's determined not to get up or stop seeking for her soul's salvation until she has found peace. "Please, God, for Christ's sake, forgive me," she pleads. "Lord, I do have godly sorrow; I'm so sorry that I failed to live for you. I will never take the Mark of total damnation; I will die first. Please, give me grace to stand," she sobs.

After several hours of earnest prayer, a light from Heaven finally shines down upon her; and Violet feels great peace and joy. Heaven's salvation fills her soul, and a shout of victory goes forth from her innermost being. Amidst all of the chaos, she has found grace in the eyes of God. Then with great humility, she says, "Thank you, dear, wonderful God, for sending your Son, Jesus, to die for me. I will stand for you and your Holy Word, and I promise never to fail you again. I know your grace is sufficient for me."

After this beautiful experience, Violet feels that she must immediately call Sal and Purple Belle to tell them the good news. She tries to reach Purple a number of times before she finally answers her phone. Purple listens intently as Violet tells her of how she found the Lord; but as she chokes back her tears, she can only stammer, "I…don't think…God… will ever accept me because I have failed Him so many times. I know His Word, but I've always broken the promises I've made to Him."

Violet continues talking to Purple for a very long time, encouraging her to cry out to God for forgiveness just as she had done; but Violet can't seem to break through to her or even convince her to pray. Finally, Violet says, "Well, Purple, I must go; but please think about what I've told you. I know the heavens seem like brass to you right now, and I felt the same way; but I was determined to pray until God answered. Now, I'm a born-new person, and I've made up my mind, Purple— no matter what I have to face, Heaven will be worth it all. I must see my sis and my mom and pop again. Bye for now, Sweetie. I will seek for God to show you mercy."

Purple feels no spirit of prayer, so she turns

on the news. The many horrors and overwhelming despair that have taken over the
Earth seem to be even worse than before,
and the same haunting report is still going
forth: "The world seems to have ended at
six o'clock this morning when hundreds of
thousands of people suddenly disappeared
from all over the world. Not one of them can
be found; and they took nothing with them,
not even their clothes. Not one suit, dress or
even a sock is missing; yet no trace of the
people can be found."

Purple knows very well what happened
because she was taught the truth. She turns
off the news and starts wandering through
the house. All the love that had once filled
it is gone, and it feels so empty. If only she
could wake up and discover that it's all just
a terrible nightmare, she would never use
drugs or alcohol again. She would give her
life to the Lord and always walk in His divine,
holy will.

Purple goes into her grandparents' bedroom,
and she notices that there's such a strong,
heavenly fragrance in the room. She wonders

what it must have been like when the cry went forth, **Behold, the bridegroom cometh; go ye out to meet him** (Matthew 25:6)! What an unbelievable moment of joy that must have been for the dearest two people on Earth who loved her the most. They had warned her so many times about the soon-coming of the Lord and how tragic it would be if she was left behind. "There's just one flight out, Child," Purple's granddad would say. "Get ready, Honey; you don't want to miss it. We have prayed so many prayers for you, and we just can't bear the thought of you being left. You know we love you so very much."

If only Purple had listened, but she hadn't. She loved the world, and she wanted to be a part of the "in crowd"; but now, she's all alone in a world of total darkness. If only she could talk to the godly pastor at Fairview; he would be able to help her, but she knows he's gone. The young evangelist who had been preaching prophecy for the past several weeks is gone, too. As she thinks about those she had seen at the church earlier that morning, she realizes, "I didn't see any of the real saints of God, those who would shout and praise His name as they sang of His blessed coming...now, that coming has happened, and they're all gone. Oh, how I pray that I will see them again."

Purple knows for sure that dear, old Mother Collins is definitely missing because she remembers seeing Jim, her only son, at Fairview weeping his heart out. She had overheard him saying that his little baby, Sue, was missing and that his dear mom was gone, too.

Purple kneels by her grandparents' bed and tries to pray, but there doesn't seem to be a God who cares about her anymore. "Oh, if only I had been ready!" She can't get this haunting thought out of her head.

Purple tries to reach Sal, but she can't get through. Then she's startled by a loud knock at the door; and she opens it to find Luther, Barry and Sidney standing there, and she completely falls apart in their arms. When she finally settles down, they talk for a while; and Luther encourages her in the Lord. She had been amazed to see Luther earlier when she was at Fairview Church. She knows that he used to teach about the prophecies of God, and it's hard for her to believe he has missed the Rapture.

After the boys leave, Purple is so miserable that she can't stay in the house any longer. She wants to find Sal, so she just starts out walking but not really caring where she's going. The air is filled with cries of sorrow, and it's like walking through a torture chamber. People keep running over to show her pictures of loved ones they want her to help them find, and she soon feels as if she'll lose her mind. She eventually finds her way to a little corner restaurant; and to her utter amazement, there is Sally inside, sitting all alone at a table by the window. Evidently, she had ordered something to eat because there was food on the table, but she was just sitting there staring into space.

Purple hurries into the restaurant; and when she gets to Sally, she cries, "Oh, Sal, I've been trying to get in touch with you, but I couldn't get through. I'm so glad I've found you!" Purple Belle sits down at the table with Sally who looks like death warmed over. "Sal, we have to face facts and go on. It's our fault that we failed to serve the Lord and have missed the one flight out. We let the devil cheat us with his ugly deceit, and now we'll have to suffer for that."

Sally looks up with tear-dimmed eyes and says, "Purple, life is no longer worth living, and I don't want to live for another moment. I've been thinking about committing suicide."

"Oh, Sal," Purple pleads, "you must never, never think like that again. What would your mother and dad say if they could speak to you from Heaven right now?"

But Sal still answers, "I don't see that there's anything to live for. I know the coming years will be nothing but torture, and the Bible says that the time will come when we won't be able to buy or sell without the Mark of the Beast."

"But, Sal," Purple pleads again, "if you don't find Jesus, you'll go to hell; and that will be much worse than being on Earth at this time. Besides, we have three-and-a-half years to decide what to do before that time comes. In the meantime, we can continue to pray that God will have mercy on us, save our souls and give us His wonderful grace that others have found and that those who made the Rapture had found. There's plenty of strength in the Lord if we can just find His favor. You have two good friends in me and Violet. The three of us must stick together and never let anything separate us." Purple is amazed at the way she's been talking to Sal; her conversation sounds like something her own dear grandparents would have said.

"Now, Sal," Purple continues, "eat something, and I'm sure you'll feel better. I'm going to order a sandwich myself. Then maybe we can look for Violet."

After eating, both Purple and Sal feel much better. Then Purple says, "Let's pay our check and get moving; I'm anxious to see Violet. She told me she has found the Lord, and maybe she can help us. She was always more levelheaded than we were anyway. She never went to the places we did, and I'm sure she never used drugs or alcohol."

Sal stands up and suggests that they first try stopping by Violet's house to see if she's there.

Outside the restaurant, the streets are still filled with insanity; and the air rings with haunting, tortured screams that can only come from tormented hearts that have completely lost all sense of reasoning. The girls begin to walk; but then they stop short when they see a man standing on his front porch, waving a handgun like a wild man and shouting, "I can't take any more of this; I have to end it all!" Purple and Sal freeze and can hardly breathe. They can't even find voice to let out a scream as the man puts the gun to his head and pulls the trigger. They both run up to his porch and then almost pass out at the gruesome sight. There is blood spattered everywhere, and it looks like he has blown half of his head off. Surely, this is just another part of their horrible nightmare that will end soon. No words could ever describe such a dreadful scene.

They put their arms around each other and run away as fast as they can. They're so frightened and in shock that they can't speak a word for at least two blocks. Then Purple finally hears Sal praying, "Oh, God, help us to get out of this hell of torture and terror."

As they continue on, people again stop them to show them pictures of missing loved ones. "Have you seen my dad...my sister...my uncle?" Mothers with empty arms and hearts cry desperately, "My baby is missing! I can't find it anywhere. Please, help me!"

Sally and Purple Belle decide to go back by way of the cemetery, thinking maybe they can get away from all of the people who are pulling on them and find a few minutes of peace. But as they start through, nothing could have prepared them for the inconceivable things they witness. Men and women are literally shrieking as they sit beside empty graves, and there are many open graves all over the cemetery.

The two girls look into one grave and see for themselves that nobody is there. As they stand there speechless, a father overcome with grief chokes out, "We buried our darling baby, Jean, just two weeks ago, and now her body is missing." But this father is so ashamed because he knows the truth and says, "We understand the resurrection of the saints took place about six o'clock this morning; and because of that, her little body is missing. My wife and I know the Bible truth about this hour; and if we had only been ready, we would be in Heaven with our darling right now. We already miss her so much."

The two girls continue silently on, their hearts bleeding for that mom and dad. They pass many more open graves—at some, the loved ones are standing over them; but at others, no one is there. One pitiful man sobs uncontrollably beside his wife's grave, and they learn that she had been a devout child of God. "If only I had been ready," he sobs without even looking up. "If only I could be with her now."

As they pass by another open grave, they can hardly believe their eyes when they see a completely distraught-looking woman let out a shrill scream and jump into the grave. They rush over to check on her; and she looks wildly up at them from the bottom of the grave shouting, "My husband was such a godly man, and now his body is gone. Why didn't I listen to him? Why was I not ready?"

The girls look around for some way to help the woman out of the grave, but they can't find anything. As they go in search of someone to help, they find the caretaker, Willie. They quickly tell him about the woman; and he just looks at them in total frustration, saying, "You girls can't even begin to imagine what I've been through since this morning. It's been like a horror movie with one wild scene after another as family members run in and out to see if the graves of their loved ones are open. It all started around eight o'clock when it was announced on the news that many of the graves in all of the cemeteries had mysteriously opened." Sal and Purple don't stick around to hear or see any more of this living nightmare, and they hurry to find the closest exit. The cemetery turned out to be no place of refuge for them, just more torment.

Both girls had heard all of their lives about the resurrection of the dead in Christ, that the bodies of the saints would rise at the sound of God's trumpet. They knew that the holy saints who were alive would then be changed in a moment and in a twinkling of an eye...but no one had ever described to them what they would face if they missed the one flight out.

After running for a few blocks, Sally and Purple Belle are gasping for breath; and stifling fear has seized their hearts. They have never before experienced such terror or witnessed such horrors. How are they ever going to survive the Tribulation Period of God's unimaginable, destructive judgments?

When the girls finally arrive at Violet's house, every nerve in their bodies seems to be on edge; and to their relief, Violet is home. They begin to tell her about all they've heard and seen; but Violet quickly interrupts them saying, "I've been watching the news, and all that's going on in this crazy world is giving me deadly chills. You just have to hear some of it."

Purple and Sal sit down with Violet to listen to the latest reports. With drawn faces and glassy eyes, the news reporters are recounting the agonizing scenes from all over the world. "Fear of the unknown makes people crazy, and people all over the world are scared stiff. They're creating mass hysteria in every country, and there's chaos on every street corner. Most people are still seeking to find an answer as to why and how millions have disappeared from the Earth. The only thing we do know now is that it happened all over the world at the same time."

The reporter continues to try to explain, "There are all kinds of theories coming in to explain this most tragic mystery and disaster in the history of man. Some people say the Rapture has taken place, but others sneer at such a thought. How could Jesus possibly have come and taken His saints to Heaven? Many professors and preachers just scoff at what the Bible says; and they claim, 'We don't know what happened, but we're certainly not dumb enough to believe that a man called Jesus who was crucified 2000 years ago made good on a promise that He would come again and take His disciples to Heaven. How can people believe such a ridiculous thought?' "

Violet turns the news up louder as the reporter states, "The simple fact is that people have disappeared into thin air. I have loved ones who are missing, and many of our viewers do, too. I have been reading the Bible, and I will confess that it seems the Bible has the only explanation to this chaos that has turned the world upside down. It had to have come from a Higher Power; there's no other way all of this could have happened. It just might be time for all of us to believe the Bible."

The girls know without a doubt that the news commentator is right. Purple Belle laments again, "If I could only find salvation." Violet has already told Purple Belle all about how she found the Lord, but she decides to tell her experience again for Sal's benefit. When she finishes, it gives the other two girls some real hope. Before they part for the day, they decide they'll meet again tomorrow and that they're going to stick together through all of this. All three of them are so alone in the midst of such a massive, worldwide catastrophe. They know they need each other, and they know they need God.

CHAPTER
FIVE

In a big city many miles from Alabesta, a young Jewish man who had a born-again mother and dad finds himself left behind. Peter's parents had found the Lord in the early part of their marriage; so he was born into a Jesus-home, and his mother and dad carefully taught him the real Gospel truth. He was rocked in a cradle of Jesus' love and tender care, and he was taught songs about Jesus from the time he could remember. One of the first ones he learned was "Jesus Loves Me."

Jesus loves me, this I know,
For the Bible tells me so.

Peter and his parents attended a good, spiritual church that taught the Virgin Birth of Christ and that Jesus was truly the Son of God. Peter's parents were filled with the Holy Spirit, so they believed and taught him 100 percent Bible truth. Peter learned that Christmas was all about Jesus, and he and his parents always enjoyed a wonderful Jesus-Christmas that was full of God's love while their other family members didn't.

Peter's parents always took him to Sunday school when he was a child, and he loved it. He had consecrated, Spirit-filled teachers who taught him so much about the Word of God. Peter was sent to good schools that didn't teach against the Word of God, and every morning the children would say the Lord's Prayer to start the day. Peter's home had a family altar; and every evening, his daddy would read some short passages of scripture before they would pray together. While Peter was in school, his parents watched him closely to make sure he associated with good young people who honored God the Father, the Son and the Holy Ghost.

As Peter grew up, they always told him, "Son, you must serve Jesus. He's the one who died for you, and there is no other name under Heaven by which you can be saved." **Neither is there salvation in any other: for there is none other name under heaven given among men, whereby we must be saved** (Acts 4:12). He was taught the fullness of the Holy Spirit; and he was also taught about the one flight out, the second coming of the Lord. His parents warned him again and again not to miss the Rapture.

Peter finished school with the highest honors and then chose to attend a college close to home. He truly loved his parents, and he didn't want to leave them at that time. He had a great desire to be a reporter and wanted a job in the news media, so journalism became his major. Peter studied hard and learned all he could about his field, and he watched successful reporters very carefully. He wanted to be the best reporter he could possibly be.

A close friend of Peter's dad, Mr. J.C. Blem,

was the editor of a large newspaper in the city where Peter's family lived; and he took a great interest in Peter. One evening, when he was having dinner with Peter's family, he told Peter that he would like to talk to him about a job when he had finished at the university. Of course, Peter was very excited to hear that.

Peter was a good-looking chap, six feet four inches tall with a nice build and hair as black as crow feathers. He always dressed neatly, and he had a likable, friendly disposition that people were attracted to. Because of that, his mother and dad felt sure he would make an excellent reporter.

When Peter finally graduated from the university, he couldn't wait to begin working. He never forgot the day when he walked into Mr. Blem's office and said, "I'm ready to become your star reporter." Then he chuckled and flashed Mr. Blem a big grin.

"Well, Son," Mr. Blem said, "it won't be easy; but I know you've been very interested in journalism since high school, and I understand you were always an "A" student. I've observed you through the years, and I think you have what it takes to become a good reporter; so I'm going to let you work with one of my best reporters, Hunter. If you work hard, you can learn a great deal from him. Be here tomorrow morning at eight o'clock sharp, and I'll introduce the two of you. He's a great guy who has been with this paper for quite a few years, and he has received many journalism awards."

When Peter met Hunter the next morning, he was just like Mr. Blem had said—a real fine gentleman who didn't seem to have any ego—and the two of them became good friends at once. Peter learned so much from Hunter; and as time passed, he did become the star reporter he had said he would be. In fact, he became one of the paper's very best; and Mr. Blem never regretted hiring him.

Peter was so totally dedicated to his job that he seemed to be married to it. The readers loved his reporting, and they thought his approach to his stories was top-notch. Most people were willing to talk to him, so he was always able to get good, useful information for his stories.

Peter was a good, moral person. He never drank, not even socially, nor did he ever experiment with drugs or run around with the wrong crowd. Peter's mother and dad admired and loved him very much, but they were well aware that his good works wouldn't take him to Heaven. His mom and dad would talk to him when they could about the end-time signs and the soon coming of the Lord. They never wanted him to forget that if he didn't get ready for the one flight out, it would be too late after it happened; but Peter never felt the need of receiving salvation.

Peter had always known the right way. Going to church with his parents was a way of life when he was growing up. He liked Pastor Huntington; he loved the good Gospel music and singing, and he enjoyed most of the young people. Nevertheless, he absolutely loved being a reporter, and his life was totally wrapped up in news. Deep down in his heart, he knew he would have to get right with the Lord one day; but he just didn't believe that Jesus would come very soon.

The weekend before the Rapture took place, Peter was working on a big story that had just broken late Sunday night; and he was the first one to arrive at the scene. Then he worked into the early morning hours of Monday so he could get his story to press ahead of the other papers.

On Monday morning, not long after going to bed, Peter wakes up with a start. It's only about seven o'clock; but he hears people outside screaming and shouting, "Come back, Jesus! Don't leave me!" Then he recognizes the voice of one of his neighbors crying, "Somebody has kidnapped my baby!" Peter's home is in a nice, peaceful neighborhood, and he's never heard anything like the turmoil that now seems to be going on outside. At first he thinks, "I must be having a nightmare; this is crazy." The thought of the Rapture never enters his mind as he gets up and raises the blind to see nothing but complete chaos up and down the street. It looks like the neighbors have all gone stark-raving mad.

Soon, Peter hears someone pounding on the front door; so he quickly puts on his robe and opens it to find Mamie Stillwell standing there in hysterics crying, "Oh, Peter, my little John is gone. All my doors and windows were locked, so I don't know how this could have happened! Please, help me look for him. He's only two years old, you know; so there's no way he could have gotten out by himself!" At that moment, a chill runs up and down Peter's spine; and he has to hang onto the door to keep from falling over. He finally manages to say, "Let me get dressed"; and he quickly closes the door.

He just stands there for a moment as one in a trance, and then he notices a strange atmosphere in the house which he recognizes to be the Spirit of God. He knows that because it's the same presence he would feel in church when the Holy Spirit would come down in a great, blessed way. Peter starts to get numb all over as he slowly stumbles toward his mother and dad's bedroom. The door is open just as it is every night; and when he enters the room, he notices the covers are still pulled up, but it doesn't look like his parents are there. Now on the verge of hysteria, he begins to shout, "Mother, Daddy, are you here?" There's no answer, so Peter throws the covers back on his dad's side and sees only his pajamas lying there; but Dad is gone. He rushes around and throws back the covers on his mother's side. Again, her nightgown is there, but she is gone. Peter immediately falls to his knees and begins to cry out, "Oh, my God, Mom and Dad have gone on the one flight out! Oh, dear Jesus, I've missed it." He keeps praying and crying as all he has been taught about true Bible salvation floods his mind. He's determined to stay on his knees and hold onto God until he receives a born-again experience.

Peter stays right by his mother and dad's bed with the Lord until he is gloriously saved. The Lord, in all of His tender mercy, has shown Peter His love and goodness; and his burden of sin rolls away just as the Bible said it would. **If we confess our sins, he is faithful and just to forgive us our sins, and to cleanse us from all unrighteousness** (I John 1:9). Peter knew that he had to be born new and quit all of his sinning. **Verily, verily, I** say unto thee, **Except a man be born again, he cannot see the kingdom of God...Ye must be born again** (John 3:3,7). He knew that when Jesus healed people, He told them to **go, and sin no more** (John 8:11). Peter had always been taught that he would have to live free from sin just as Jesus did when He was here on Earth, and he knew that Jesus taught living free from all sin.

Peter weeps and cries until he just can't cry any more. He loves his mother and dad so much, and he doesn't know how he will ever live without them. He's sure their good pastor is gone and assumes that most of the church members have gone on the one flight out, too.

"Oh, dear Lord," he cries again, "I thought I had plenty of time! I could have been ready, and it's no one's fault but mine. Mom and Dad made sure I knew the truth, but I do thank you, Lord, for saving my soul. I will serve you, and I will never take the Mark of the Beast. I won't let the devil deceive me ever again. I know his Mark is the Mark of doom and that if I take it, I will blaspheme against the Holy Ghost. Jesus, I know you said when you were here that there's no forgiveness in this life or in the life to come for a person who blasphemes against the Holy Ghost." **But he that shall blaspheme against the Holy Ghost hath never forgiveness, but is in danger of eternal damnation** (Mark 3:29).

Peter doesn't know how long he has been crying and praying, but there is one thing he does know—that he has definitely reached Heaven. However, he can't stop thinking about what a fool he has been when he was raised by such wonderful parents who clearly showed him the way to Heaven.

Peter's thoughts are soon interrupted by his phone ringing and several knocks on the door. At first, he doesn't answer either one; but the calls keep coming in, and there continues to be one knock after another. Finally, Peter decides to answer the phone, and he's surprised to hear Mr. Blem on the other end.

"Peter, is that really you?"

Peter manages a weak, "Yes, it's me."

"Your dad and mother aren't there, are they?"

The tears start to flow again as Peter chokes out, "No sir, they're gone. You do know that the Lord came for His people this morning, don't you?"

"Unfortunately, Son, I do; and you can't imagine how many calls we've had about it. That's why I'm calling you. I felt sure that your parents would be among the missing, and I thought maybe you would be gone, too. At different times, your parents would talk to me about Jesus coming for His children. They were such wonderful people, and I know they were ready. I'm just so sorry now that I never gave their words serious consideration." Mr. Blem falls silent for a few moments; then he quietly says, "Surely, you remember my daughter's little four-year-old boy, Jimmy. My wife and I are crazy about him, and now he's gone. I don't know how we're going to live without him, and my daughter and her husband are nearly out of their minds with grief.

"Perhaps you haven't listened to the news yet," Mr. Blem continues, "and I hate to ask you this when you must be feeling absolutely horrible, but would you come in and write a story about the missing Christians, babies and little children?"

Peter doesn't answer for a moment because he can't imagine doing such a thing at this time.

"Are you still there, Peter?" Mr. Blem asks anxiously.

"Yes, I'm here."

"Peter, I know you were taught right, and it will mean so much more to the readers for a good Jewish reporter to write the story. If you decide to do it, you can feel free to include the Holy Scriptures to show people that you have proof of what you're writing about. I don't have another reporter who can write the story as intelligently as you can. You were taught the Bible, and you're not blind to what has happened today. I know you're going through the deepest valley of your entire life right now; so I'll let you think it over, and you can let me know."

Peter really doesn't feel like writing or even know what to say, but he does know that people need the truth; so he finally tells him, "Give me a few minutes to pull myself together, and I'll come in and give it a try."

"Thank you, Peter," Mr. Blem graciously says. "Your parents would be proud of you because I know I am. I've admired you and your work for years."

With that, Peter manages to say goodbye and hang up. Then he starts praying, "Oh, God, please help me. I promised you that if you would save me, I would do anything for you; and I know people need to have their eyes opened to the Gospel truth."

Peter somehow manages to get dressed and make his way through the crowded streets; and when he arrives at the office, Mr. Blem is relieved to see him. He'd already heard the newsboys on the street shouting the latest headlines: "Read all about the greatest tragedy and mystery to ever strike the Earth! People all over the world disappeared at about six o'clock this morning!"

As Peter listens to all of this, he knows he has the answers people need; so he prays, "Dear Jesus, help me to write this story like you want it written. People are calling this great event that took place a mystery; but all they have to do is read their Bible, and it will tell them exactly what's going on...and that things will get worse on tomorrow."

After praying, Peter begins to write, "The sudden and tragic disappearance of people all over the world is not a mystery. Turn to the Word of God and read I Thessalonians 4:13–17 and I Thessalonians 5:1–9. These scripture passages plainly tell us that Jesus will come for His saints one day, and that day arrived Monday morning at six.

"Jesus said He would come as a thief in the night. **Ye, brethren, are not in darkness, that that day should overtake you as a thief** (I Thessalonians 5:4). The Lord also said, **Ye are all the children of light, and the children of the day...Therefore let us not sleep, as do others; but let us watch and be sober** (I Thessalonians 5:5,6).

"My mother and dad taught me the Holy Bible and lived according to its teachings, and they're gone. I'm left here because I wasn't ready. Just like all of you, I wasn't serving the Lord; and now we're all left behind.

"People all over the world are hysterical with fear and screaming that their babies have been kidnapped, but that's not so. Jesus came and took all the babies and the little children to Heaven along with all the adults who were born again and living holy, pure and clean.

"I'm not out searching for my mother and dad because I know where they are—with Jesus. Just as God took Enoch to Heaven alive because he walked with God and pleased Him, my parents too went to Heaven alive. **By faith Enoch was translated that he should not see death; and was not found, because God had translated him: for before his translation he had this testimony, that he pleased God** (Hebrews 11:5).

"The Lord said we are to come together and reason with Him. **Come now, and let us reason together, saith the LORD** (Isaiah 1:18). When we reason with God, we find that Jesus foretold of this miraculous event when He was here—that all the born-again Christians, all the babies and all the small children would disappear at one time from all over the Earth. Now, we have to get down to business with the God who created us and seek His forgiveness for all sin and disobedience. We must get ready to live holy before Him throughout this great Tribulation Period no matter what happens.

"St. John's Gospel says, **If I go and prepare a place for you, I will come again, and receive you unto myself; that where I am, there ye may be also** (John 14:3). Jesus also said, **Therefore be ye also ready: for in such an hour as ye think not the Son of man cometh** (Matthew 24:44).

"Jesus told of many signs that would occur just before His return; and then He said, **When these things begin to come to pass, then look up, and lift up your heads; for your redemption draweth nigh** (Luke 21:28). He told us there would be wars and rumors of wars. **And ye shall hear of wars and rumours of wars: see that ye be not troubled: for all these things must come to pass, but the end is not yet. For nation shall rise against nation, and kingdom against kingdom: and there shall be famines, and**

pestilences, and earthquakes, in divers places (Matthew 24:6,7). He said dangerous times would come and that people would be **lovers of pleasures more than lovers of God; Having a form of godliness, but denying the power thereof** (II Timothy 3:4,5). The power that so many people have denied is the very power they need to be saved and to live holy, the power they need to be able to accept God's truth and miracles and to recognize the wickedness in these last days that the Lord foretold of.

"People, there is no need to search for your loved ones who are missing. In this story's opening scriptures, the great Apostle Paul gave us the answer to what is being called 'the greatest mystery ever to strike the Earth.' Where did Paul get his information?—from the God of Heaven, of course. The Bible warned us that in the last days scoffers would come, walking after their own lust **and saying, Where is the promise of his coming? for since the fathers fell asleep, all things continue as they were from the beginning of the creation** (II Peter 3:4)."

When Mr. Blem reviews Peter's explanation, it astounds him beyond words; and he's quite sure it's one of the most outstanding pieces Peter Fench has ever written. He orders the paper to go to press at once, and then goes to tell Peter how pleased he is. "Peter, thank you for the fabulous and insightful explanation. I'm sure it will help many, many people. I know this has been a rough day; so you can go now if you'd like, and I'll see you tomorrow."

Although Mr. Blem has never been saved, he respects the Bible and believes that it's the infallible Word of Almighty God. He believes Jesus was a child of the Holy Ghost and was born of a virgin.

As Peter hurries home, the sights he sees are appalling and disturbing. He has witnessed many horrible scenes in his work as a news reporter, but nothing compares in any way to what he's now seeing all around him. Parents are frantic and crying aloud for help in finding their missing children, and boys and girls are praying to find their parents.

Peter is relieved to get back home and seek

solace in the house he has always loved so much, but it now feels so empty because all the love is gone. The two people who had loved him so much and had always made time for him are missing, gone to Heaven on the one flight out. Again, the tormenting thoughts fill his mind, "How stupid I was. I could have gone with them, and we would be together right now. Oh, Mother and Dad, you taught me nothing but the truth. You were persecuted so much down through the years, even by your own family members; but you never seemed to get upset—you just prayed for them...and for me."

Peter sinks to the floor, buries his face in the carpet and cries his heart out. Finally, weak and exhausted, he manages to get up and turn on the TV. As he watches the unbelievable aftermath of the Rapture, he exclaims, "My Lord and my God, this Earth has been completely turned upside down! It is indeed reeling to and fro just like God said it would through His great prophet Isaiah." **The earth shall reel to and fro like a drunkard, and shall be removed like a cottage; and the**

transgression thereof shall be heavy upon it; and it shall fall, and not rise again (Isaiah 24:20).

People can't get over the catastrophe that has swallowed up the whole Earth, and many of them are committing suicide because it's too much for their minds to take. No words could ever express the mental torment, and people feel that killing themselves is the only way they'll find any relief or be able to escape the world; but Peter knows better—that suicide is the devil's way, not God's way.

As Peter continues to watch the reports, he's so grateful that his mother and dad not only taught him God's truth but lived it; and he's thankful they will never have to endure any of this tragedy. Peter will always be haunted by the thought that he could have gone with them, and he still doesn't know how he's going to make it without them.

Peter doesn't think anyone could have ever had sweeter parents than he did, and he's so thankful that they're together today. They loved each other so much and never argued or fought, so he'd had a marvelous home filled with pure, human love as well as divine love. "Oh, God, why didn't I listen? I had always intended to give my life to you one day, but I thought I had plenty of time. Now, I realize how valuable time is...but it's too late."

The news reports take Peter from one nation to another. It's an endless flood of nothing but fear, heartache and despair on a scale never seen before. Everything is so beyond the imagination that it just doesn't seem it can be real. It's like having a never-ending nightmare from which you can't wake up.

Peter notices that some people have made their way to the TV studio. Some stumble in like they're drunk; some look like the walking dead, and others are continually screaming, "Somebody help me!"

One desperate woman shoves herself in front of the camera holding a picture and pleading, "Here's my darling baby in the arms of my precious husband. They're both missing, and I hope that somebody watching this program has seen them. Oh, please call this studio right away if you have any information!"

Suddenly, she begins to shake all over and screams, "I can't take it without my baby and my husband any longer!" Then before anyone can stop her, she pulls out a handgun and blows most of her head off. What a ghastly sight! Peter is stunned as he watches people faint all over the studio, and they immediately begin clearing everyone out. Peter can hardly believe what he has just seen as he turns off the TV and sits there in silence wondering, "What's going to happen to all of these people?"

By this time, it's getting late; and Peter gets ready for bed as the many disturbing thoughts of the day roll over and over in his mind. He begins to pray for God's wisdom and guidance in the days to come and eventually nods off into a restless sleep.

Peter still feels tired when he wakes up Tuesday morning, but he forces himself to get out of bed and get ready for work. The city is still in an uproar as he makes his way to the office; and sadly, he realizes that things will never be the same. When he arrives, he notices a note from Mr. Blem on his desk asking to see him right away; so Peter hurries over to his office and knocks on the door.

"Mr. Blem, it's me, Peter."

"Come on in, Peter; I've been waiting for you. First of all, how are you doing, Son?"

"I'm making it, but I really miss my mom and dad."

"They were very special people, Peter; and I'm sure you'll always miss them. Well, the reason I called," Mr. Blem continues, "is first because you're my favorite reporter and second because you're Jewish, and I know your parents taught you the prophecies concerning the Jewish nation; your dad often spoke to me about them. As you're well aware, Peter, the false christ—the so-called superman—is going to speak to the world Wednesday morning at nine; and people will be able to tune in by TV, radio, satellite or the Internet. Of course, all of the newspapers of any size will carry a recap of what he has to say; but I want you to do a big story for our paper that's over and above that—one on who this king, Daniel's little horn, really is. Will you do it, Peter, or do you need time to think it over?"

Peter pauses for a moment before he says, "Sir, the reason I hesitated is that it's going to be dangerous to come out against this man. I'll be glad to write the article, but you'll have to promise to keep it anonymous."

"I understand completely, Son, and I promise you that your name will not be included. I know, Peter, that you're the only one who knows how to study the prophecies of Daniel and gather the valuable material you'll need for your report. Just give me a call when you're finished."

Peter gets up to leave and says, "I'll get to work right away; I know you want to include it in a special edition."

As soon as Peter gets back to his office, he starts working. He goes to the book of Daniel and chooses the scriptures he will need. Then he assembles the rest of his material and begins to write: "Dear Readers, the new world dictator is scheduled to speak to the world Wednesday morning; but don't let him be a mystery to you. The great prophet Daniel plainly told us of this false christ, who he called the little horn, in the prophecies God gave him. **I considered the horns, and, behold, there came up among them another little horn...and, behold, in this horn were eyes like the eyes of man, and a mouth speaking great things** (Daniel 7:8). When this false christ speaks, he will indeed pretend to know everything there is to know in the entire world; but his power comes from the devil, and he will deceive and destroy people.

"**Seventy weeks are determined upon thy people and upon thy holy city, to finish the transgression, and to make an end of sins, and to make reconciliation for iniquity, and to bring in everlasting righteousness, and to seal up the vision and prophecy, and to anoint the most Holy. Know therefore and understand, that from the going forth of the commandment to restore and to build Jerusalem unto the Messiah the Prince shall be seven weeks, and threescore and two weeks: the street shall be built again, and the wall, even in troublous times. And after threescore and two weeks shall Messiah be cut off, but not for himself: and** the people of the prince that shall come shall destroy the city and the sanctuary; and the end thereof shall be with a flood, and unto the end of the war desolations are determined. And he shall confirm the covenant with many for one week: and in the midst of the week he shall cause the sacrifice and the oblation to cease, and for the overspreading of abominations he shall make it desolate, even until the consummation, and that determined shall be poured upon the desolate (Daniel 9:24–27).

"The Antichrist will make a covenant with the Jewish nation for seven years; and in the middle of those seven years, he will break the covenant and set himself up in the temple of God in Jerusalem, showing himself not to be the Son of God but God Himself. Then the Jews will flee from him into the wilderness where the real God of Heaven will have prepared a safe place for them.

"The Jews have waited thousands of years for their Messiah and suffered seemingly endless persecutions, and they'll think they have found their Redeemer at last; but, in reality, he will be this: **A vile person, to whom they shall not give the honour of the kingdom: but he shall come in peaceably, and obtain the kingdom by flatteries. And with the arms of a flood shall they be overflown from before him, and shall be broken; yea, also the prince of the covenant. And after the league made with him he shall work deceitfully: for he shall come up, and shall become strong with a small people. He shall enter peaceably even upon the fattest places of the province; and he shall do that which his fathers have not done, nor his fathers' fathers; he shall scatter among them the prey, and spoil, and riches** (Daniel 11:21–24). He will divide the spoil among people all over the world, and those in need of money will flock to support him and accept him as Lord God Almighty.

"**And at that time shall Michael stand up, the great prince which standeth for the children of thy people: and there shall be a time of trouble, such as never was since there was a nation even to that same time: and at that time thy people shall be**

delivered, every one that shall be found written in the book (Daniel 12:1).

"In Revelation 19, the superman, or Daniel's little horn, is called the Beast. **And the beast was taken, and with him the false prophet that wrought miracles before him, with which he deceived them that had received the mark of the beast, and them that worshipped his image. These both were cast alive into a lake of fire burning with brimstone** (Revelation 19:20). The Beast, also called the Antichrist, and the false prophet will be cast alive into the lake of fire which is burning with brimstone.

"**And the devil that deceived them was cast into the lake of fire and brimstone, where the beast and the false prophet are, and shall be tormented day and night forever and ever** (Revelation 20:10). The devil will be cast into that same lake of fire to be tormented day and night forever. This, however, will not take place in the middle of the seven years of great Tribulation but at the end, after the Battle of Armageddon.

"When the Beast breaks the covenant with

the Jewish nation, he will then require all people to have the Mark of the Beast. You won't be able to buy or sell without the number of the Beast—666—but you must know that it's the Mark of doom...and God will never forgive anyone who takes it."

Later that afternoon, Peter calls Mr. Blem and tells him the article he requested is finished; and Mr. Blem is surprised to hear from Peter so soon. "You mean your article is ready to go to press?"

"It just needs your approval, and it's ready to go," Peter assures him. "I really don't think you'll want it to be any longer. Would you like me to run it over to your office?"

"That would be great! Give me about five minutes and then come on over."

When Peter arrives, Mr. Blem proudly says with a smile, "Come on in, Peter, and let's go over your story." Mr. Blem reaches anxiously for the article and begins to read as Peter carefully studies his expression. He knows that when Mr. Blem likes something, it always shows on his face; and Peter has worked with him long enough to know when he is definitely pleased.

After a few minutes, a smile of approval spreads across Mr. Blem's face; and Peter is relieved to see that his story has passed what the staff calls "the Blem test." When Mr. Blem finishes reading the entire article, he looks at Peter in amazement and declares, "You have certainly done an excellent job! I'm sure most of our readers are like me, and they don't know much about the book of Daniel; so I'm sure the alarming yet timely prophecies you have included will startle them enough that they'll study them for themselves. Hopefully, this superb write-up will also draw new readers to our paper.

"Now," Mr. Blem continues, "let's come up with an eye-catching headline." Peter pipes up immediately with, "The Superman Is a Fake"; and Mr. Blem agrees wholeheartedly. He can just hear the paper boys shouting, "Read all about the great superman! The evidence is here to prove he's a fake!"

Then Mr. Blem suddenly becomes very serious and says, "Peter, this story is sure to send people straight to the book of Daniel because you've given them the exact chapters and verses to read. Of course, we know that those who don't want to believe won't; but rest assured that many people will accept this warning and be alert to what's going on. You've done a far better job on this story than I ever expected, and my promise is still good—your name will not appear anywhere in connection with the article."

"I'm anxious to hear what the arch deceiver has to say in the morning," Peter comments. "I'm sure he'll declare that he alone has the answers for all the world's problems and that he'll bring peace and prosperity to all." Then Peter gets up and says, "Mr. Blem, if that's all you need from me, I'll be going. I still have more work to do, and the day is going fast."

"No problem, Peter. I'll talk to you tomorrow."

When Peter had been working on his first story the day before, he had talked to one of the reporters at the TV station he most often watches. In light of what he has just written, he calls back again. When the secretary answers, he says, "I'm the reporter who called yesterday and talked to reporter Hollis about what the Bible says concerning the mystery that took place Monday morning, and I have some very important additional information that he must have." The secretary senses that the call is important and gets Hollis right away.

"Hollis, I'm so glad I've reached you. This is Peter Fench from the paper; we talked yesterday. I'm sure you're already aware that the so-called superman will appear on radio and television satellites throughout the world tomorrow morning, but you must also know that he is the false Christ. I was born Jewish, but my mother and dad converted to Christianity before I was born and accepted the real Jesus. I know from the Bible that this false Christ is going to make a covenant with the Jewish nation for seven years. The prophet Daniel explains all about it, and he describes him as Daniel's little horn. **I considered the horns, and, behold, there came up among them another little horn, before whom there were three of the first horns**

plucked up by the roots: and, behold, in this horn were eyes like the eyes of man, and a mouth speaking great things (Daniel 7:8).

"After the Antichrist makes a covenant with the Jews, he will break that covenant in the middle of the seven years (Daniel 9:27) when he sets himself up in the temple and declares himself not to be the Son of God but God Himself (II Thessalonians 2:4). The Jews will then realize that they have been deceived and will flee for their lives to get away from him (Revelation 12:6).

"Tomorrow, you'll hear this so-called superman say that he'll make the economy to prosper; and then he'll promise to do something that no dictator has ever done before—he'll divide the spoil with the people, and they'll go crazy over him (Daniel 11:24).

"Hollis," Peter continues, "I just wanted you to be able to let your viewers know what's going on, so I hope you will find this information helpful."

"Thanks, Peter," Hollis replies. "I appreciate your thoughts, and I'll see what I can do with all of this."

When they hang up, Peter is happy that he was able to reach Hollis again. He just wants to make sure people are given the truth, whether they read the paper or watch TV.

Peter's parents and his church had taught him the truth about the Antichrist and what was to come, so he knows that the world church will rule with the Antichrist for the first three-and-a-half years and that in the middle of Daniel's week of years [seven years], the covenant with the Jews will be broken. Peter knows that everything about the devil's superman is false, that he will speak things which are full of darkness but will then shine the devil's false light on them and convince people that he has all the answers they need.

Peter finishes the rest of his work for the day and then heads home. As soon as he walks in the door, he turns on the news to hear Hollis talking about the false superman. "Tomorrow morning at nine," Hollis reports, "the so-called superman will appear on this station. However, a reporter called me today to say that before we tune in, we should read the book of Daniel in the Bible. He said that book explains all about this dictator who will claim to have the answers to everything and that Daniel was a prophet of God who received everything he wrote straight from God. If you want to look any of this up," Hollis continues, "you'll find it in the ninth and eleventh chapters of Daniel as well as in some of the other chapters. Daniel called this superman the little horn and said he is an arch deceiver."

Peter turns off the TV because he just can't take any more right now. He begins walking through the house, but it seems so big and empty now. He finds himself in his parents' bedroom again...oh, if only they were here! He falls to his knees and begins to pray, thanking God again that his parents had taught him about the real Christ and that Jesus is now in his heart.

In the midst of his prayer, he feels an overwhelming urge to go to church. It's the first time he's felt like going since all of this began; and since it's still early evening, he gets in his car and drives slowly through the crowded streets. It still feels like a nightmare to see the crowds of people crying, praying and pleading with others to help them. Many try to stop him in his car, but he doesn't dare stop. He knows they'll eventually have to come into the knowledge of the Bible truth—that their loved ones are in Heaven, caught away to be with the Lord forever.

Peter is shocked when he finally makes it to the church and sees that the parking lot is filled with cars and that many more are lined up and down the street. He's just in time to see someone pulling out of the parking lot, and he hurries to grab the empty space. He decides to enter the church from the pastor's side entrance, and he's relieved to find it unlocked. As he winds his way through the pastor's office, he can hear people praying and crying out to God; and when he opens the door into the main auditorium, he sees that the altar is filled with people while others are kneeling and crying at their seats.

As Peter looks around to see who has been left, he spots Patsy Gardner, a girl Peter has known from the time she was born; and he figures she must be about fifteen years old by now. Just then, she looks up and sees him, too. She's shocked at first, but then she smiles and quickly makes her way over to grab him and give him a hug. "Oh, Peter, I can't believe you've been left, too; all of this is just so terrible. I know how devout your parents were and that they were ready for the one flight out. My parents and sister are gone, too. I've cried and prayed until it seems like I can't cry or pray anymore, but thank God I do feel sure that I've found Jesus and that He has forgiven me."

Peter's heart bleeds for Patsy, and he wants to be certain about her soul; so he asks, "Are you sure you've really found Jesus?"

"Oh, yes!" she assuredly answers. "Thanks be to Jesus for saving our souls! But what am I supposed to do now?"

"We have to continue praying that we will be ready for what's to come," Peter answers, "and we have to make sure others are ready, too."

"Do you remember Suzanna Hilton?" Patsy asks. "She's about my age with long, dark brown hair. Well, she's been left, too. Her dad died a few years ago, and her mother and two brothers are missing. I talked to her a short while ago, and she's in pitiful shape. Her aunt was left, and she came here with her tonight. She said that she has cried and prayed so much, but she can't believe the Lord has forgiven her. You know, Peter, we're so blessed that we attended this church, one that preached nothing but the truth."

Peter is really impressed with Patsy's insightful words. "Think about it, Peter," she solemnly continues, "we're going to have to face seven years of Tribulation. I'm glad we're not in darkness and that we know the truth about the awful time we're now in. At least we have the assurance that we can still go to Heaven and see our parents again. Peter, would it be all right if I go and get Suzanna? She desperately needs help."

"Of course," Peter kindly responds. "Bring her aunt, too, if she'll come. I'll go into the pastor's study; you can meet me there."

Patsy joyfully turns to go find Suzanna while Peter heads into the pastor's study where he still feels the holiness and sacredness of the Lord. He sits down at the pastor's desk and notices some sermon notes lying out. As he begins to read them, he's totally amazed to see that the topic for the Sunday night that has just passed was "One Flight Out." Peter's heart seems to stop beating for the moment, and then he continues reading. The message contained in those notes warms Peter's heart so much that it's just as if the anointed man of God is standing right there talking to him.

Peter was in church nearly every Sunday night as well as the many other service nights, and he absolutely loved the beautiful music and singing. But this past Sunday night, Mr. Blem had scheduled a special meeting that he wanted all the reporters to attend. Peter has always been so grateful for all the help Mr. Blem has given him, so he didn't feel he should miss it. Since Peter had become such an excellent reporter, Mr. Blem had always counted on him and would give him some of the best stories; so Peter chose to attend the meeting rather than go to church.

As Peter ponders all of this, the office door

opens; and in walks Patsy with Suzanna and her aunt. Suzanna is so glad to see Peter; but when he gives her a big hug, she breaks down in tears. She's so tormented and carrying such a heavy load. Peter gives Suzanna's aunt a welcome hug, too, but she doesn't look much better than Suzanna. After a few moments, everyone seats themselves in front of the pastor's desk; and Peter takes a seat on the other side so he can look them in the eyes as they talk.

He begins by saying, "We all know very well that Jesus has come, and we have missed the one flight out. Thankfully, Patsy and I have found Jesus as our Lord and Savior and have been born new. The Bible clearly tells us that Jesus was born to the Virgin Mary, a child of the Holy Ghost; and in Acts 4:12, it says that there is no other name under Heaven whereby we must be saved. Jesus is the only foundation we must have, and He went to Calvary and gave His life for all of us. That's why salvation doesn't come by works but by faith in the divine blood of Jesus. **For by grace are ye saved through faith; and** that not of yourselves: it is the gift of God: Not of works, lest any man should boast (Ephesians 2:8,9).

"Jesus gave His blood so we could have His divine nature, and the Bible says He came to make us sons and daughters of God the Father. **But as many as received him, to them gave he power to become the sons of God, even to them that believe on his name: Which were born, not of blood, nor of the will of the flesh, nor of the will of man, but of God** (John 1:12,13). Jesus is our elder brother, and He died to give us eternal life. Because Jesus lives, John 14:19 says that we'll live also; and we'll never die."

Peter is surprised at his own words. This is definitely a new experience for him as he continues addressing Suzanna and her aunt. "If you would like, Patsy and I will pray with the two of you; and the Lord Jesus will forgive you of all your sins. The Bible tells us that if we believe in Christ, He will make us a new creation in Him. **Therefore if any man be in Christ, he is a new creature: old things are passed away; behold, all things**

are become new (II Corinthians 5:17). Jesus brought the **new and living way, which he hath consecrated for us, through the veil, that is to say, his flesh** (Hebrews 10:20).

"Now, if you will, please stand up and say the sinners' prayer with me. 'Oh, dear Jesus, I'm so sorry I disobeyed you and didn't get ready for the one flight out. You said if I would confess my sins with godly sorrow, you would save my soul. I am so sorry, Jesus, that I sinned against you; but I have come home, and I will serve you the rest of my life. Come into my heart, Jesus! Come on in! I believe I am now a child of God and that I have let Jesus in.' "

Peter looked at Suzanna and her aunt and said, "If you meant that prayer, Jesus has come in. Now you can say, 'Hallelujah, Jesus has come! Hallelujah, Jesus is mine! I'm going to Heaven one day! I will never take the Mark of the Beast. I will serve Jesus with all of my heart.' "

All four laugh and cry together because they're so jubilant and happy that they have found Jesus as their personal Savior. At last, they're on their way to Heaven. Peter thinks to himself that he's so glad he came here tonight.

Peter goes on to instruct Suzanna and her Aunt Flossie how important it is for them to pray, fast and live in the Word. Then he says, "We'll continue to meet here at the church. I'm sure Pastor Huntington would be happy to know how we're using the office that was his for so many years. Feel free to bring others with you who need salvation and want to find Jesus, but please bring them in one at a time. We don't want to overcrowd the office because we won't be able to work as well to get them saved if we have too many."

Peter sets their next meeting time for tomorrow evening at eight o'clock and then reminds them, "Don't forget to tune in Wednesday morning at nine. The false christ—that so-called superman who claims to have all the answers—will be on TV. Before then, you should read the book of Daniel so you'll know what God told His great prophet about this man. The Bible calls him different names; but in Daniel, he is referred to as Daniel's little horn."

They all embrace once more and then go their separate ways. Peter again goes out the pastor's private entrance, the same way he had come in, so as to avoid the crowd. Once outside, he's amazed at how light and free he feels. He knows Jesus has wrapped His loving arms around him and that the Lord is using him to win the lost for the Kingdom of God. If only Mother and Dad could see this; they'd be so proud. Then he stops and thinks, "Maybe they do know. The Bible does tell us that the angels rejoice over every sinner who repents (Luke 15:10), so Heaven has to know some things about what's going on here."

As Peter draws near his home, there is still chaos everywhere. People haven't settled down at all as they continue crying and searching for missing loved ones and showing their pictures to everyone they meet. He hears the same questions over and over again—"Have you seen my baby? Have you seen my mother? Can you look at this picture and help me?" Needless to say, Peter is glad to get home where it's quiet.

Years ago, Peter's dad had bought a piece

of adjoining property and had put in a private road that led to the back of their original lot from a street a block away. He had also installed a high fence at the back of the yard with an automatic gate so no one would have to get out of the car when arriving home. Peter is more thankful for that now than ever before because he can come and go without running into all the crowds.

Peter knows that he will now have to adjust to a different life. His mother and dad were usually both there when he would come home in the evening. Mother would have dinner ready, and he always enjoyed spending time with them...but now they're gone. If only he had been ready. He walks through the house thanking God that he's still alive and able to help bring lost souls to Jesus. He considers it such a miracle that Jesus has given him salvation, the passport to Heaven.

Peter is well aware that God has looked out for and protected him. He also knows that if God had not looked out for his mother and dad before he was born, they would have missed the one flight out; and he probably never would have gotten saved. All three of them would have been like the rest of the Jewish nation—deceived by the Antichrist. But thank God, his mother and dad knew the real Christ, the Son of the mighty God of Heaven; and they had taught him about Jesus. Again he prays, "Oh, precious Jesus, I'm so sorry that I was such a shameful disappointment to you; but I'm here now to do your whole will. I have no selfish motives; in all my waking hours I will seek to be just what you want me to be."

Peter's thoughts then go to the fact that his dad and mother left him a lot of money, and he knows he will have to keep the Antichrist from getting his hands on it. Peter's dad had told him more than once, "Son, your name is on everything your mother and I have. You never know when there might be an accident or a tragedy that would take our lives, and I believe it pays to be safe. Of course, we hope that doesn't happen; but you know where we keep our cash money and all of our important papers just in case."

Peter knows he will need the Lord's help to

safeguard the money, so he turns his mind to something more important than the money— studying God's prophecies. His mother and dad had studied God's Holy Word every day, and they had marked special portions of His prophecies in their Bibles that he wants to go over.

Peter studies late into the night; and although he's exhausted, he has God's peace and full assurance in regards to getting the money out of the different banks and investment companies. He knows he will need it to be able to help people who don't take the Mark get food when the time comes that they can't buy or sell. In the midst of his thoughts, Peter finally falls asleep.

CHAPTER
SIX

Peter's amazed to wake up Wednesday morning refreshed through and through. He first praises God for the souls He helped him to win the day before and then asks God to give him more souls at church tonight. He knows very well that there are other young people who had been regulars at church but had not been consecrated and ready for the one flight out. He has the names and numbers of a few of them, so he tries to call them and invite them to meet with their small group. The first girl Peter's able to reach is Thelma; but when she answers, she's so overcome with grief that he can't understand a word she's saying. He tries to comfort her so she'll stop crying and they can talk; and after a short while, she does settle down somewhat. Then Peter asks, "Thelma, did your family make the Rapture?"

"My mom and dad are missing," she sobs, "but my two brothers are here with me; and we're torn to pieces. We don't know what to do because we never thought Jesus would really come in our day."

"I know exactly how you feel," Peter breaks in. "My mother and dad made the one flight out, too; and I'm all alone. I decided to go to church last night, and I was amazed to see the place filled with people crying and praying. I had already found the Lord Monday morning at home by seeking God with all of my heart. I was determined to hold on to Him until He saved my soul. Now, I know without a doubt that I'm saved. Thank God!

"You and your brothers can get saved, too," Peter encourages. "Then if you'll serve the Lord, you can meet your mom and dad in Heaven and be with them for eternity. God helped me to get two people saved yesterday in the pastor's study, and I'd like you three to meet me in the pastor's study at eight o'clock tonight. Jesus is your only hope now because we're beginning the seven years of the Tribulation Period, and things are just going to get worse and worse. All of you have been taught the Bible, so you know I'm telling you the truth. What do you think, Thelma? Can you and your brothers come?"

"Oh, Peter," she gladly replies, "we'll be there; you can count on it! The boys are scared to death, so I know they'll be glad to come. Thanks so much for calling. I really appreciate it because we sure do need help."

Peter encourages her some more and then reminds her to tune in at nine to see the so-called superman. "But remember," Peter warns, "he's an absolute fake. He's Satan's man, and I'm sure you'll feel an overwhelming amount of the devil's power drawing you to him as he speaks; but you can't give in to it. I want you children to know what you're up against."

Peter decides not to make any more calls

because he wants to study the Bible and pray before the false christ appears to the world. Nine o'clock comes quickly; and Peter turns on the TV just as the news commentator announces, "In a moment, you'll hear a man who has seemingly come out of nowhere and claims to be the Christ, the very Messiah the Jewish nation has been looking for for so many years. We don't know anything about him; so we'll let you listen to what he has to say, and you can make up your own mind. Now, without further delay, here is the man who claims to be the Christ with all the answers."

With that, the Antichrist appears; and he is far beyond anything Peter ever imagined. The dark, oppressing presence of the devil is so strong in the room that Peter has to cry out to God to help him so he won't give over to his powers. Peter knows God gave him the story for the newspaper and that He led him to just the right scriptures to back up the fact that the Antichrist is indeed a false christ. Peter hopes people will heed his words and read about the false christ for themselves in the eleventh chapter of Daniel. He wants them to know that for the first three-and-a-half years, this superman will bring about peace; but it will be a false peace.

Peter's thoughts are interrupted as the Antichrist begins to speak: "Ladies and gentlemen, I am here as the savior of the world. I have all the powers of Heaven behind me, and I have come to bring peace at last to the world. I promise to work so that all the nations throughout the Earth will prosper. I am rich in divine power, so I don't need money; and I will divide the spoil with all people. Many of you aren't working and can't find jobs, but I'm going to change all of that. Give me a little time, and I'll prove to you that I keep my promises. I will be signing a covenant with the Jewish nation today, and they're so excited about it because they have looked for me for such a long time."

As Peter continues to watch, he feels the devil's power getting stronger and stronger, trying to draw him to the screen; so he centers his mind on the divine blood of Jesus, and the drawing power begins to back off. He's so grateful for the divine blood because it makes all the difference in the world.

The Antichrist wraps up by saying, "This is my message to all of you for now; so watch my every move as I show the whole world that I AM real, and I DO have all the answers."

Peter feels as if he's frozen to his chair; the Antichrist's power was so much stronger than he ever expected. Then the announcer reappears and says, "You have heard the great superman. Now we'll all have to watch and see what happens. Maybe during his next announcement he'll give us some answers about our loved ones who have disappeared; so stay tuned to this station, and we'll continue to give you updates about this superman as soon as we receive them."

Just as Peter switches off the TV, the telephone rings; and it's Mr. Blem. "Well, Peter," he acknowledges, "you told it like it is. That man said everything you wrote, and you even included much more information than what he said. Once again, thank you for the work on your extraordinary write-up; we should sell lots of papers today. You won't need to come in again until tomorrow; I'm sure you have plenty of things to do, so goodbye for now."

Peter hangs up and then sits there in a daze thinking about the superman's announcement; it makes the Tribulation Period all the more real to him. However, he knows he can't sit there all day, so he forces himself to get moving because he has a lot to do. He first checks the family safe where he knows there is a large sum of money. Then he goes to the lower level of the house where his dad had buried a bigger vault in the floor. Peter has trouble finding it, so he knows it'll be nearly impossible for others to find unless they know exactly where to look.

Inside the vault, Peter finds investment papers regarding hundreds of thousands of dollars in bonds as well as in gold and silver and even more cash money than what was upstairs. Peter knows that in the first part of the Tribulation Period, he will have to cash in everything he can and draw out all the money so he will be able to use it later in the underground black market. Even now, he's aware that there is an underground market for many things; so he's sure that one day there will be an underground market for food and water. God has blessed Peter and his family, and he wants to use those blessings to save others from taking the Mark of the Beast.

Peter's dad had kept money in five different places—three banks and two loan companies. Thank goodness, none of them suspected anything or asked any questions when Peter went in, drew out all the money and cashed in all the bonds. The people in these organizations knew Peter's dad well, and they were familiar with Peter, too, because he had made many trips to the banks and loan companies with his dad. Also, Peter's name had been included on all of the assets and investments.

By mid-afternoon, Peter has successfully closed all of his dad's accounts and cashed in most of his investments. He doesn't bother to add up all the millions he has accumulated, but he does know he will use most of it to help others.

Peter puts all the money in the big vault hidden under the lower level. He reasons within himself that if someone breaks in to rob him and discovers the safe with a few thousand dollars in it, they'll be satisfied and never think to search for another vault. On top of that, he has a great alarm system and a couple of big dogs that act as excellent guards. Peter's done all he can today to make sure most of the money is safe and secure, and he feels very relieved.

Throughout all of this, Peter's phone has been ringing almost constantly. He hasn't answered it because he figures it's probably just people wanting to ask about or know who wrote the article on the superman in the newspaper. Peter feels the article gave people sufficient information, and he doesn't want to discuss it any further. Instead, he wants to take time to pray and seek God.

When Peter finishes praying, he finally decides to check his messages; and he finds there are a few from Mr. Blem. He thought that was odd since Mr. Blem had already told him he didn't have to come in, so he calls him back.

"Peter, my boy, I'm so glad to hear from

you. I've been trying to reach you because I have a big favor to ask. I know I already told you that you wouldn't have to come in today, but people are calling us nonstop with questions about Daniel's little horn. Obviously, many took your advice and began studying Daniel, but they're confused about the references to the little horn in chapter eight; and we just don't have the answers for them. Can you help clear up any of this?"

"Wow, Mr. Blem," Peter says with amazement, "I can't believe people have actually taken time to study Daniel that closely. That just tells me that God is working with them, and that's exciting. I'm really over my head today, but it looks like I'll have to write a short explanation about this. You see, Mr. Blem," Peter explains, "the little horn referred to in chapter eight is actually Antiochus Epiphanes, a type and shadow of the Antichrist, the superman who introduced himself this morning."

"Peter," Mr. Blem says with relief, "I knew you would have the answer. How quickly can you get something written?"

"Well, I already have a meeting at church this evening, and I have to be there. I'll tell you what; I'll work on it as soon as I hang up, and then I'll give you a call after church."

"That sounds like a plan," says a very grateful Mr. Blem. "I'll wait for your call later tonight; don't worry about what time it is."

They hang up, and the first thing Peter does is thank the Lord for another opportunity to spread the truth. Then he goes to Daniel, chapter eight to gather the verses he'll need and begins writing.

"Wednesday morning, Daniel's little horn, the Antichrist, addressed the world; however, don't confuse him with the little horn referred to in the eighth chapter of Daniel. Both of them are significant in understanding Bible prophecy—one represents the superman, the Antichrist; and the other represents Antiochus Epiphanes, a powerful tyrant who ruled from 175 B.C. until 164 B.C. Study chapters seven and eight of Daniel closely until you can separate the two little horns.

"The Lord gave Daniel the prophecy of the Antichrist first, but he didn't receive the prophecy of the first little horn, Antiochus, until the Lord gave him a vision two years later. In that vision, recorded in the first part of chapter eight, God told Daniel about Antiochus and explained the meaning of the first little horn to him. In Daniel 8:23, the prophecy again turns to the latter days and the reign of the Antichrist.

"The Bible tells us that the first little horn came forth while Greece was in power, so it could not possibly be the little horn of the Antichrist who has now come forth in this great Tribulation Period. Again, the first little horn is Antiochus.

"The ancient kingdom of Babylon had great power as well as did the kingdom of the Medes and the Persians and that of the Greeks; but Antiochus was a ruler who was much more cruel than the others. Up until his reign, no king was ever described as having such power.

"During his reign, Antiochus desecrated the temple of Jerusalem. **Yea, he magnified himself even to the prince of the host, and by him the daily sacrifice was taken**

**away, and the place of his sanctuary was
cast down** (Daniel 8:11). Antiochus enraged
the Jews. He set up a statue of Jupiter in the
temple's holy of holies, robbed the temple,
forbade circumcision, destroyed all the sacred
books that could be found and commanded
the unholy sacrifice of swine. In the days to
come, you must know that you will also see
the Antichrist desecrate the Jewish temple in
Jerusalem.

"For more information about Antiochus and
his eventual downfall, refer to the book of
the Maccabees. It recounts the deliverance
of the Jews from the extremely oppressive
Antiochus. Judas Maccabeus fought and
finally retook Jerusalem, purified the temple
and restored the daily sacrifice. After Antiochus had desecrated the altar of God in 168
B.C., 2300 days passed before Judas Maccabeus and his brother finally delivered the
Jews. This was the fulfillment of the prophecy
in Daniel 8:13,14 which says that the sanctuary and the host would be trodden underfoot
for that length of time before God's house
would be cleansed.

"Chapters seven and eight of Daniel must be looked at as a double prophecy or we will miss what God is trying to tell us. These prophecies are (1) for the period of time of Antiochus Epiphanes and (2) for the period of time of the Antichrist, the great Tribulation the world is now in."

With the Lord's help, Peter finishes with just enough time to gather his thoughts and get to church. Peter's parents had always been very strict about him being on time, so he doesn't want to be late.

When he arrives at church, he's happy to see that all of the kids have arrived on time as well and that everyone seems genuinely happy to be there. After exchanging hugs, Peter begins. "Last night, I prayed with Suzanna and her Aunt Flossie; and they both found Jesus. Now, Thelma, you and your brothers have been taught about Jesus, and you know very well that He loves you and will forgive you. It's bad enough to miss the one flight out, but it will be much worse if you also miss Heaven because then you'll be lost for all eternity. I'm sure you would all like to see your parents again, wouldn't you?" All three of them quickly nod their heads in agreement.

Then Peter asks, "Would all three of you please come up here and stand before the desk? I would love to pray with you; but when you say the sinners' prayer, you have to mean it. Only then will God, for Christ's sake, forgive you. Jesus said if you will confess your sins, He will forgive you; but He can only do that if you come to Him with godly sorrow. That means you have to be as sorry that you committed your sins as God is that you committed them.

"Please say this prayer with me right now: 'Oh, God, I'm so sorry I have sinned against you.'" With hands raised, all three of them pour their hearts out to God. "'I'm so sorry that I missed the one flight out. Please, forgive me. I believe in the blood of Jesus and that He died on Calvary for me. I believe that His divine blood washes away all of my sins. Come into my heart, Jesus! Come on in!' Now, if you meant that prayer, say, 'Hallelujah! Jesus is mine!' "

Peter encourages them to really praise the Lord; and when their hearts are filled with God's love, he says, "Now, you can go and help others find Jesus. Can you hear the cries going up at the altar in the main auditorium? Each one of you needs to go out there and pray with different people. When you find some you feel are really sincere in seeking the Lord, ask them to come back here to the pastor's study; and I'll pray with them. When they find the Lord, they'll be happy in Jesus, too; and you'll be blessed for helping them."

With joyful hearts, the three new born-again souls make their way into the auditorium; and after a short while, they begin to bring sincere people in one by one. Then Peter helps each of them to find the glorious salvation they need, the soul-cleansing salvation that was born in Bethlehem many years ago.

At one point, Patsy runs into the office all excited and says, "Peter, the people want you to come out and talk to them. They want to know the truth about what has happened."

Peter is graciously overwhelmed at the

opportunity to speak for his Lord; so he takes his place in front of the congregation and begins, "People, I know you're really troubled and that your world has been turned upside down. None of us ever thought we'd face anything like this; and unfortunately, it's a mystery to most people. They're coming up with all kinds of theories, but the truth is what counts; and you can only find that truth in the Word of the living God.

"The Bible says, **In such an hour as ye think not the Son of man cometh** (Matthew 24:44). Jesus Himself said, '**If I go** [away]...**I will come again, and receive you unto myself** (John 14:3).' But He also warned us about our souls. **I would thou wert cold or hot. So then because** [if] **thou art lukewarm, and neither cold nor hot, I will spue thee out of my mouth** (Revelation 3:15,16).

"Jesus gave us the signs to look for just before He would return, and God tells us in the Bible that He would gather the Jews from every nation and bring them back to their homeland. Today, that prophecy has just about been fulfilled. The Bible also said that the end-time would not come until there was a great falling away from the truth, and we've all seen that happen. **Let no man deceive you by any means: for that day shall not come, except there come a falling away first, and that man of sin be revealed, the son of perdition** (II Thessalonians 2:3). Our churches have dried up, and very few ministers preach the true Gospel of Jesus Christ.

"Jesus came for His own this past Monday morning at six o'clock. The Bible tells us, **For the Lord himself shall descend from heaven with a shout, with the voice of the archangel, and with the trump of God: and the dead in Christ shall rise first: Then we which are alive and remain shall be caught up together with them in the clouds, to meet the Lord in the air: and so shall we ever be with the Lord** (I Thessalonians 4:16,17).

"I'm so sorry I wasn't ready to go. My mother and dad raised me in this church because they knew the pastor preached and lived the true Gospel of Jesus Christ. Jesus plainly told us that the Gospel must be preached to all nations, and then the end would come. **And this gospel of the kingdom shall be preached in all the world for a witness unto all nations; and then shall the end come** (Matthew 24:14).

"When I woke up the other morning, I discovered that my loving parents were missing. Instantly, my mind was thrown into such a state of agony that I thought I would die. How could I possibly live without them? When I realized the Rapture had taken place, I knew there was no need to search for them—they had gone to Heaven with the Lord. I'm so thankful that I knew enough to drop to my knees and cry and pray until Jesus saved my soul, and He will do the same thing for each one of you if you really want Him to. Don't you want to go to Heaven and see your loved ones again?" Peter pleads. "If so, why don't you say the sinners' prayer with me right now?"

At this point, the people are ready to receive; and Peter invites them to the altar. People flock down the aisles, and others are on their knees all over the auditorium; so Peter knows that they really mean business. Once they all gather, he warns, "You must mean this prayer; and after we pray, I want you to stay here and seek God until you are truly delivered through the blood of the Lamb."

After Peter leads them all in the sinners' prayer, it's time for him to go. As he walks back through the office on his way out, he runs into some of the young people who have just gotten saved. He tells them he'll be back again tomorrow night at the same time and encourages them to come and to invite others.

Peter hurries home; and as he had promised, he calls Mr. Blem to tell him the new article is finished. Since the deadline for the next day's paper has already passed, they agree to meet first thing in the morning. Peter has had such a grueling day that he literally falls into bed and is asleep in no time.

Bright and early Thursday morning, Peter is in Mr. Blem's office reviewing his work on the first little horn, Antiochus Epiphanes. Once again, Mr. Blem is more than pleased with his work and even gives him a small bonus to thank him for all of his efforts over the past few days. Peter is very grateful, and he knows that he will add it to what he has already stashed in his home vault for the days to come.

After leaving the office for the day, Peter still has a few hours left to deal with the few remaining bonds and securities that he hasn't yet cashed. His dad had seen to it that they were all good, solid investments, so he has no trouble cashing them in for a good profit.

Peter knows it's not wise to carry such a large amount of cash, so he heads straight home and puts it safely away in the big vault. He's so amazed at the peace the Lord has given him about everything, and he isn't afraid anymore. He knows the path he must follow, and he knows he has the money to take care of himself and others. His heart is filled with love and thankfulness to the good Lord.

As the days go by, Peter studies day and night to learn all the Bible has to say about the seven years of Tribulation and its ultimate end—the deadly Battle of Armageddon. Being a top-notch reporter, Peter knows how to gather facts and put them together; so he carefully studies Daniel, Ezekiel, Isaiah, Jeremiah, Joel and Revelation. Then he puts all of the facts together to get a true picture of the whole seven years of the Tribulation.

He knows it all began with the one flight out, and he feels so fortunate to have found Pastor Huntington's notes on prophecy in his office. Oh, what a godly man that pastor was! The more Peter pores over the pastor's notes on the Rapture, the sorrier he is that he missed the pastor's last message that Sunday night before Jesus came. When Mr. Blem called a special meeting that night, Peter felt that he just had to be there; but maybe he'd be in Heaven right now if he had decided to go to church instead.

As Peter continues studying Pastor Huntington's notes, he's astounded by all of the different prophecies the pastor had come into the knowledge of, ones God's true prophets had received in past years from the Father in Heaven. Peter already knew that the world church would believe the Antichrist, and the people are doing exactly that. Peter watches the world church totally embrace the fact that the superman doesn't believe in the Virgin Birth, living free from sin or the one flight out; and he sees that the world church has completely joined hands with the Beast.

All of this makes Peter realize that he will have to work harder than ever to get every person saved he possibly can, and he becomes very bold. He continues to go to the church where he grew up in the truth and encourages people in the ways of the Lord. A good number of the young people, like himself, had been deceived by the devil and left behind; and careless adults had been left as well.

Peter's church is on fire for the Lord, and people disgruntled with the world church begin coming to the services when they hear Peter is helping people find the Lord. Some have loved ones missing who they know had been living holy before the Lord without spot, wrinkle, blemish or any such thing. Those loved ones had tried many times to persuade them to serve the Lord in the right way, but they wouldn't listen. Now, however, many of them are finally ready to listen.

Peter continues to study hard the things Jesus had to say about the Tribulation time he's in, and he tries to be at church every night to pray with people. It never ceases to amaze him at how many people are coming to the Lord, but he knows it's because their church is filled with the great anointing of God. Most of the regular members made the one flight out, and they left behind the mighty anointing that still lingers in the building. Peter thanks the Lord every day for that anointing and how it's moving.

Peter has continued his work at the newspaper; and because Mr. Blem was so astounded with his two stories on the false superman and the first little horn, he can't stop talking to Peter about them. The paper has received many phone calls and letters regarding them, and they have convinced Mr. Blem to really study the book of Daniel for the first time in his life.

One day, Mr. Blem sends for Peter to come to his office where he receives a welcomed shock that blesses his soul. Peter walks in and sits down, expecting to receive a new assignment; but he can hardly believe his ears when Mr. Blem says, "Peter, I want you to pray with me so I can be saved."

Peter has grown to really appreciate Mr. Blem, but he'd never thought he would win him for the Lord; so no one could be happier than Peter is to hear that Mr. Blem is ready to repent. He breaks down and begins to cry as he bares his soul to Peter and admits, "I just can't get over the disappearance of my grandson. Your dad mentioned the one flight out to me several times, and now I'm so sorry that I didn't show any interest. I've been studying you, and I've seen how much you've changed since you found the Lord... and I see how miserable I still am. I know I need God's help."

Peter explains to Mr. Blem that the Holy Spirit is dealing with him, and then he invites him to say the sinners' prayer. Mr. Blem is so sincere and ready that he can hardly wait to start, and he confesses all of his sins with many tears. Then he begins praising the good Lord because he knows his burden has rolled away, and he's free!

Mr. Blem can hardly contain his joy and relief as he says, "Now, Peter, I want you to pray for my wife, my daughter and her husband. They can't get over little Jimmy being gone either, and they just cry continually. It's been extremely hard on all of us."

Of course, Peter is always happy to pray for people; and he asks, "Why don't you come to church tonight at eight? It will really help you and bless you to pray with God's people. I'd be happy to stop by and pick you up."

"I'd like that very much," Mr. Blem replies with the smile of a free man, "...and, Peter, you can call me J.C."

When they arrive at church that evening, it's filled and running over; and as usual, Peter goes in through the pastor's study. Some of the kids who were saved the night before have others with them who also want the Lord's salvation. As Peter begins to pray with them, J.C. is filled with God's joy; and he praises the Lord because others are finding the true Christ of God. J.C. then follows Peter to the auditorium; and for the first time, he sees people seeking the Lord with their whole hearts. Peter stays later than usual this night because his boss seems to be enjoying the service so much.

They finally leave; and when Peter is saying good night to J.C., he offers, "If your wife would like to go with us tomorrow night, I can come by to pick you both up around 7:45. Please tell her that we would love to see her." As Peter leaves, he wishes his parents could see how the Lord is moving for the Blems because they had prayed so many prayers for them. The couples had known each other for years and were the best of friends.

The next night, Verdie Blem does go with them; and she too finds God and the peace she's been looking for. She's gloriously saved, and Peter is even more overwhelmed by all God is doing. The congregation keeps requesting that he speak and tell them more about salvation and the power of God. Peter is shocked to discover that so many people don't know what a true born-again experience is through the blood of Jesus Christ.

As Peter takes J.C. Blem and his wife home this night, he feels compelled to tell them that they should draw their money out of the bank and cash in any bonds or investments they may have. He even offers to put their money in his vault if they have no safe place to hide it. "You must know," Peter says with great concern, "that the Antichrist will take everything when he breaks the covenant with the Jewish nation. The Mark of the Beast will be forced upon the world, and you won't be able to buy or sell anything unless you have the Mark. **And he causeth all, both small and great, rich and poor, free and bond, to receive a mark in their right hand, or in their foreheads: And that no man might buy or sell, save he that had the mark, or the name of the beast, or the number of his name** (Revelation 13:16,17).

"If you take the Mark of the Beast," Peter continues, "you'll be damned for eternity; it will cost you your soul. If you have any money stashed away, you will at least be able to buy certain things on the black market to survive. I've already drawn all of my parents' money out of the bank and cashed in all their investments and securities, and I've hidden them safely away.

"Take the time to study the book of Revelation. It plainly tells you that in the middle of the week, which means the middle of the seven years of Tribulation, the Mark will be forced upon all people. After these first three-and-a-half years are over, the Antichrist will set himself up in the temple of God in Jerusalem, declaring himself to be God—not the Son of God, mind you, but Lord God Almighty Himself.

"At that time, all peace will be gone; and destruction will begin throughout the whole world. We'll have to take our church meetings underground, and many people will be arrested. Those who don't take the Mark will be put to death while thousands of others will die of starvation because they won't have the money to buy from the underground.

"Well, good night to both of you, and please give all of this some sincere thought. Mrs. Blem, I'm so glad that you have found Jesus; and I'll be glad to pick you both up again tomorrow night if you want to go back to church."

"Thank you, Peter," she graciously answers.

"You have been so kind, but I think we'll drive ourselves tomorrow night and try to get our daughter and son-in-law to come with us."

Peter's delighted to hear that and adds, "If they do come, please bring them to the pastor's study where J.C. and I were last night; and I'll do my best to make sure they're saved. They must realize that receiving salvation is the only way they will ever see their little boy again. Have a good night, and I'll see you tomorrow at eight."

Peter is overflowing with God's joy as he drives home. God's great mercy and blessings are really something for him to behold, and he just can't thank the Lord enough for the godly mother and dad he had—parents who raised him to recognize and honor God. He's also so grateful to God for saving J.C. and Verdie. "God, do help all of us to stand true," he whispers to the Lord.

When Peter gets home, his dogs come running to greet him; and he's glad that he at least has them to keep him company. After feeding them and playing with them for a little while, he drops into bed.

The next night, J.C. and his wife do bring their daughter and son-in-law to church. Both of them are still totally consumed with pain and agony over the loss of their little boy, but Peter is able to help them and explain to them how they can go to be with Jimmy for all eternity. They eventually settle down and accept the truth, and then they give their hearts to God and are gloriously saved from all of their sins. What a victorious day in the Lord it has been as they all leave the church that night truly happy in Jesus!

CHAPTER
SEVEN

The days pass, and things begin to settle down somewhat as people adjust to their changed lives. Plenty of people continue searching for the missing Christians in hopes of finding their children and loved ones, but they're no longer running hysterically through the streets at all hours. The world church continues to accept all the Antichrist wants them to, and they unashamedly obey him in everything. But there is one lingering question on the minds of many people throughout the world: "Why is no one having any babies?" The answer, of course, is that

God has made the human race sterile; and He won't allow one baby to be born for the entire seven years of the Tribulation Period. God knows the children would be just like their parents, and He wants no more sin-filled human beings on the Earth.

The Antichrist keeps promising people that babies will come, but it's a promise he has no power to keep. Nevertheless, he's busy trying to make good on his many other promises. Jobs are made available to people all over the world, and the poor have never had it so good. He robs the rich of their money and gives the spoils to the poor, and this convinces the poor that he really is the Son of God. Millions are swept into his arms of deceit, and people all over the world begin talking about how remarkable he is. Many think the savior of the world has truly come.

The world continues to spiral deeper and deeper into sin; and soon, nearly all the preachers are taken over by the devil. The Antichrist even begins dictating what can and cannot be preached from the church pulpits. People who have knowledge of the Bible and

God's ways quit going to the so-called houses of God because they know they're nothing but evil. People who want to worship the true God in Spirit and in truth have to go underground with their services, but most people are content in their sin and degradation.

Just when things seem to be going so well in the world's eyes, the Antichrist shocks the inhabitants of the Earth by breaking the covenant he had made with the Jews after only three-and-a-half years. True to the prophecies of God in His Holy Scriptures, the Beast sets himself up in the temple of God in Jerusalem, showing himself not to be the Son of God but the Almighty God of Heaven and Earth.

Who opposeth and exalteth himself above all that is called God, or that is worshipped; so that he as God sitteth in the temple of God, shewing himself that he is God (II Thessalonians 2:4).

And he shall confirm the covenant with many for one week: and in the midst of the week he shall cause the sacrifice and the oblation to cease, and for the overspreading of abominations he shall make

it desolate, even until the consummation, and that determined shall be poured upon the desolate (Daniel 9:27).

Luther knew all along that this would happen, but he's still astounded when it actually takes place. The first three-and-a-half years of the Tribulation Period have seemed to fly by for Luther; and now he knows that the worst is just around the corner.

One evening as he listens to the news, he hears the announcement he's been dreading since the Tribulation Period began: "Tomorrow, you will no longer be able to buy or sell anything, draw your money out of the bank or do any business whatsoever anywhere in the world unless you have the Mark of the Beast—666. The Beast has declared that nobody will be excused; everyone must have the Mark."

Luther knows all too well that this is according to the Word of God. **Here is wisdom. Let him that hath understanding count the number of the beast: for it is the number of a man; and his number is Six hundred threescore and six** (Revelation 13:18).

The newscaster continues, "Many want to

know what the Mark will cost, and the answer is that it will be free of charge. Convenient receiving stations are now being set up in many cities, towns and villages. Just look for the sign that reads, 'Take the Mark here.' Once you have the Mark, you can freely do business; but until then, you won't even be permitted to buy food or water. We all need to eat to survive, so please make plans to get the Mark right away."

Luther shouts back to the newscaster, "But you don't understand that it will cost you your soul! If people take that Mark of doom, they'll be damned forever. There will never be any forgiveness for them, and they will have blasphemed against the Holy Ghost!" Luther is disgusted with the news media's lack of knowledge, but he's also petrified. He knows he'll have to stand firm for God, but he also knows that starvation will be a terrifying monster to face.

Luther doesn't want to hear any more of this, so he shuts off the TV; but a short time later, he tunes in again for the evening report. The commentator seems to be totally up in arms as she reports in a high-fevered pitch, "An extraordinary event happened today that has never been seen on Earth before. Two men appeared—or at least they look like men—but never has any man had power like these two do; and they declare that they have come down from Heaven to preach the Gospel of Jesus Christ. If any man attempts to hurt them, fire shoots forth from their mouths and instantly destroys their persecutors. They can fly through the air seemingly at the speed of light, and it's as if they can appear all over the world at the same time."

Luther knows that Revelation chapter eleven describes these two men as being God's witnesses who He said would come down from Heaven. **And I will give power unto my two witnesses, and they shall prophesy a thousand two hundred and threescore days, clothed in sackcloth. And if any man will hurt them, fire proceedeth out of their mouth, and devoureth their enemies: and if any man will hurt them, he must in this manner be killed** (Revelation 11:3,5). As Luther listens, he says to himself, "God can do anything, and He's proving it to the world in this final hour."

The news commentator continues, "All who have heard and seen these men are completely petrified, and they have already killed many; but they appear to only attack those who have the Mark of the Beast. Regardless, whoever or whatever they are, I don't see how they can possibly be human. The soldiers in the Beast Regime are terrified of them, and even the Beast himself is deathly afraid. No one has any power over them because they have power that no human beings have ever had before. The Beast and his deadly regime thought they had power and authority over all men on Earth, but they can't touch these two men...that is, if they really are men."

Luther talks back to the commentator again saying, "Don't you know the truth? They're men from Heaven."

The commentator continues, "These men are shaking the Earth, and stifling fear has gripped people all over the world. It's not yet clear why these men seem to hate all who have the favor of and worship the Beast, but we do know that they're ready to kill every soldier of the Beast Regime who comes against them. It was reported earlier today that 1000 soldiers of the Beast Regime went up against these two witnesses—as they're called—and when fire shot out of their mouths, all of the soldiers were immediately destroyed. It's beyond the imagination to think that men could have such destructive powers without using any weapons."

Luther sits in awe watching the witnesses in action and seeing the deadly scenes they have caused around the world. Their powers of destruction are ferocious, and nothing can stand in their way. Luther thinks to himself, "In light of what I've just seen, it's no wonder people with the Mark are afraid to go out on the streets. According to the Bible, these witnesses will be on the Earth for three-and-a-half years. Just think of the millions with the Mark of the Beast who could be killed in that time."

For weeks, stories of the death and destruction caused by the two witnesses dominate the news; and each new report of Beast

Regime members dying makes Luther's heart shout within him because the Beast Regime is bringing such suffering, torture and death to people throughout the Earth. They have indeed become the world's worst nightmare; and they have caused nothing but terror, heartache and despair since the Mark of the Beast was introduced.

Many people are so overcome with fear that they can't even think clearly enough to make decisions, and they're terrified of what even the next hour will bring. The Beast Regime has been given the power to arrest anyone they want for any reason, and they have already killed multitudes throughout the Earth. Now, at last, this deadly regime that has put petrifying fear into the hearts of people all over the world stands helpless before these two men.

Luther isn't afraid as he watches the two witnesses; and he's actually excited to see that the Christians are getting some valuable help from Heaven. He's amazed as he watches the news clips of them flying through the air without wings and preaching the Gospel of Jesus Christ with a boldness never heard before. "You must be born again to go to God's Heaven," they fervently declare. "Jesus is the true Son of God come down from Heaven, the one who died on the Cross for the sins of all people. You must accept this message of salvation now because there is no other way to Heaven but through the blood and the name of Jesus."

Yes, people are scared of the witnesses, but they're also fascinated by them; so the reports continue. "The two witnesses can fly through the sky at will, and their message is being heard by all people throughout the Earth—a message they claim is of the eternal Gospel. Just seeing these two in action is enough to give anyone nightmares; but you can't help being totally astounded as you watch them land and take on a band of the Beast Regime's army, destroying tens or even hundreds of soldiers with just one flash of the consuming fire that spews forth out of their mouths.

"These men also have the power to call down any kind of plague at will; there's definitely never been anything like them in the history of man. It seems that they can just will to be anywhere on Earth, and they're there in a split second. It's absolutely incredible! Many people are beginning to admit that these two must have come down from Almighty God in Heaven to have such power."

Luther gets excited every time he hears a report about the witnesses spreading the Gospel, and he can just imagine how upset the Beast must be with such reports: "Besides calling all men to salvation, these witnesses boldly warn, 'Don't take the Mark of the Beast. It will seal your destiny and damn your soul just like the devil and his kingdom are damned. Be willing to give your life if you must, but don't take the Mark. Repent of your sins today; and, for the sake of His Son, God will hear you and save your soul. If you're later tortured and killed because you won't worship the Beast, all the suffering will be worth it because Heaven will be yours for eternity. Never forget that no one has ever loved you like Jesus loves you, and no one has ever cared for you like He cares.' "

Luther loves to hear the witnesses quote

Revelation 12:11 because he knows that's the secret. **And they overcame him by the blood of the Lamb, and by the word of their testimony** [or the Word of God that they put in their testimony]**; and they loved not their lives unto the death.** Luther knows that all Christians can overcome the Beast with the divine blood. Then his mind goes to some of the great prophets who had prophesied about the mighty, overcoming power of the blood, and he thinks of the many true preachers in the past who had declared salvation only comes through the blood of the Lamb.

Luther never thought he would hear such glorious preaching again, but he rejoices as the message goes forth to uncover the Beast and his terrorizing regime. Luther knows that the devil and all his demons are powerless to hold back the Gospel message that the witnesses are proclaiming to the world.

As Luther leaves the house one day, he hears the witnesses begin to declare a new message: "Thousands of Jews have accepted Jesus Christ as the real Messiah." Luther is elated because he knows this is yet another prophecy being fulfilled. Just as the Bible had foretold, 144,000 of the Jews had been born new and caught up to Heaven as the first fruits of the Jewish harvest for Christ.

Many supposed biblical scholars are bewildered because they had claimed that the 144,000 would evangelize the world; but Luther knows the truth, and he knows that doctrine isn't biblical. Mount Zion is in Heaven; so the 144,000 had to have been caught up into Heaven, and they can't possibly preach the Gospel to the world from Heaven. **And I looked, and, lo, a Lamb stood on the mount Sion, and with him an hundred forty and four thousand, having his Father's name written in their foreheads. And I heard a voice from heaven, as the voice of many waters, and as the voice of a great thunder: and I heard the voice of harpers harping with their harps: And they sung as it were a new song before the throne, and before the four beasts, and the elders: and no man could learn that song but the hundred and forty and four thousand, which were redeemed from the**

earth [redeemed from the Earth into Heaven]. **These are they which were not defiled with women; for they are virgins. These are they which follow the Lamb whithersoever he goeth. These were redeemed from among men, being the firstfruits unto God and to the Lamb. And in their mouth was found no guile: for they are without fault before the throne of God** (Revelation 14:1–5).

Luther rejoices over this because the 144,000 missing Jews are truly the first fruits unto God and to the Lamb, God's Son. In order for them to follow the Lamb—Jesus—as the prophecy states, they have to be in Heaven because Jesus is in Heaven at this time.

During all of this, not only are the witnesses preaching the Gospel of Christ but angels are as well; and the whole world can hear them. **And I saw another angel fly in the midst of heaven, having the everlasting gospel to preach unto them that dwell on the earth, and to every nation, and kindred, and tongue, and people, Saying with a loud voice, Fear God, and give glory to him; for the hour of his judgment is come: and**

worship him that made heaven, and earth, and the sea, and the fountains of waters (Revelation 14:6,7).

In addition to spreading the salvation Gospel, they're also warning the world of God's judgments. **And there followed another angel, saying, Babylon is fallen, is fallen, that great city, because she made all nations drink of the wine of the wrath of her fornication. And the third angel followed them, saying with a loud voice, If any man worship the beast and his image, and receive his mark in his forehead, or in his hand, The same shall drink of the wine of the wrath of God, which is poured out without mixture into the cup of his indignation; and he shall be tormented with fire and brimstone in the presence of the holy angels, and in the presence of the Lamb: And the smoke of their torment ascendeth up forever and ever: and they have no rest day nor night, who worship the beast and his image, and whosoever receiveth the mark of his name** (Revelation 14:8–11).

As the second three-and-a-half years of the

Tribulation Period get well underway, more and more prophecies of God are being fulfilled all the time. Angels are now not only preaching the Gospel all over the world, but God is also using them to pour out the wrath of His tormenting judgments on the Beast and his kingdom and on all those who have taken the Mark.

Luther studies the book of Revelation more now than ever before so he'll know exactly what's coming. One day, his studying is interrupted by a booming voice that seems to shake the whole Earth. He runs outside and looks up to see a big angel preaching in the sky. As he stands there in awesome wonder, it dawns on him that the whole world can see and hear this angel at the same time. Luther lets out a shout of praise because his God is showing all mankind that He is Lord God Almighty. One way or the other, He's making sure that everyone in the Tribulation Period hears His Holy Word. All those with the Mark of the Beast try everything they can think of to keep from hearing the Gospel message, but they can't do it.

CHAPTER EIGHT

During the first three-and-a-half years of the Tribulation Period, Dr. Morehead was consumed with seeking to deceive every person he could about the Rapture and trying to convince the people that the Antichrist is the true Christ. He boldly preached against the Virgin Birth of Christ, and a devilish smirk would cross his face any time the subject came up. He had become one of the most prominent leaders of the world church, and that church had become more degraded than ever since they had joined hands with the Antichrist—the man of sin and Daniel's little horn. Now, the world church is spewing out all kinds of false doctrines that are against the Bible.

The Antichrist has accomplished exactly what Daniel had prophesied he would; and by peace—although it was a false peace—he has destroyed many. He has become the most revered man in the world because no one has ever before divided the spoil with the people, and he has truly caused craft to prosper throughout the Earth. Most of the people on Earth truly believe that he has all the answers to every problem, yet there are still those whom he has not been able to deceive because they know the truth—that the seven-year covenant he has made with the Jews is not going to last...and it doesn't.

The world church arrogantly ruled with the Antichrist for the first three-and-a-half years; but true to Daniel's prophecy, the Antichrist breaks the covenant after those three-and-a-half years. He desecrates the Jews' holy temple by setting himself up in the temple of God in Jerusalem and claiming to be Lord God Almighty, and this is completely revolting to the Jews.

The news of such a despicable act explodes like a bombshell throughout the world, and it's immediately followed by another announcement that shakes the inhabitants of the Earth—the introduction of the Mark of the Beast which is 666. **Here is wisdom. Let him that hath understanding count the number of the beast: for it is the number of a man; and his number is Six hundred threescore and six** (Revelation 13:18).

During all of this, Dr. Morehead has been busy traveling to many different countries, representing the world church and the power of the Beast. After returning from one such world meeting with agnostics, infidels and unbelievers who are full of devils and false doctrine, he decides to hold a similar event at his own church.

Since Dr. Morehead has become such a well-known minister, all of the news media carry the details of his upcoming event: "Come and join world renowned minister Dr. Morehead for a special event. He's one of the most knowledgeable ministers in the world church, and he has all the answers you will ever need for today. That church and the Antichrist have successfully joined together to form a partnership of great power which is strictly against the doctrines of the Bible. They say that the Antichrist is the true redeemer, and they're doing all they can to prove to the world that Jesus Christ was and is the greatest deceiver the world has ever known.

"Dr. Morehead has just completed a string of successful meetings in other nations, and he has returned home with much to share. He will begin a series of sermons that all should hear as he brings forth great teachings for the world today. Don't miss it!"

All the true Christians are completely appalled at this announcement because they know the sermons will be full of false doctrine; but the devil's deceit is powerful, and Dr. Morehead's church is completely packed the first night. There are even crowds of people standing outside who can't get in. Luther is one of those in the congregation that night because he wants to hear what kind of lies

Morehead will spew out.

Most people are anxious to know if he has any new information concerning the adults, babies and small children who had disappeared from the Earth over three years ago. No worldly explanation has yet been given for this still-baffling mystery.

Old Dr. Morehead enters the pulpit in his usual pompous style and immediately turns some people off when he begins telling them how ignorant, devilish and unlearned they are. This prompts a lot of hissing and creates a big disturbance in the crowd. Many of Morehead's ex-members are there, and they're well aware of how he had deceived them for many years with his false teachings and misinterpretations of the Gospel and that his deceit caused many of them to miss the Rapture.

Many of the people remember how that years ago, he had run his own godly mother out of the church because she had stood up in a Sunday morning service to give a testimony of praise to God. He was so cruel and heartless that he called her a fanatic in front of the whole congregation. Then he told her to leave and never come back. She was such a sweet child of God, and it broke her heart; but she did leave and began attending Fairview.

Many members of the Beast Regime are in the audience this night to protect Dr. Morehead and to keep order, but the crowd will not settle down. He has hurt and deceived so many throughout the years that they begin throwing things at him and screaming accusations at the top of their lungs. "He robbed us of our children, our babies and our mates! He caused us to miss the Rapture, and he should pay for that with his own life!" By this time, people are becoming more violent and throwing whatever they can get their hands on.

Someone hits him right in the face with a big, overripe tomato, and the crowd begins to laugh as it splatters all over him. Morehead is completely humiliated, and he loses it. He starts cursing like a wild man, and the blasphemies pour out of his mouth in a never-ending stream. He starts yelling to the members of the Beast Regime, "Arrest all those who don't have the Mark and force them to take it or be put to death!"

Mass chaos breaks out all over the church, and the cruel and heartless soldiers of the Beast Regime rise up and start unmercifully beating the people with clubs. These soldiers' only mission is to maim and kill those without the Mark, and the place suddenly looks like a war zone. They knock people's teeth out, break their bones and even blind some with their inhumane blows. People all over the auditorium are covered with blood.

Suddenly, in the midst of this struggle, two men appear; and a deadly silence falls over the crowd—the two witnesses have arrived! A shrill whistle pierces the air; and a devilish, mocking voice shouts, "All soldiers of the Beast Regime, be aware that the two witnesses who claim to be from Heaven have just arrived; and they think they can destroy us."

Most of the soldiers are too afraid to mock the witnesses, and they back away in sheer terror. However, one arrogant soldier runs up and strikes one of the witnesses, and that unleashes his deadly power. Fire immediately shoots out of the mouth of the witness and kills the soldier before he even has time to scream. The fire flashes again and again; and each time, more soldiers are killed. Others start moving in to help those who are dying, and they're torched as well. Soon, there are piles of dead bodies everywhere.

Morehead doesn't seem to understand the fear the Beast Regime soldiers have for the two witnesses, and he can't believe what's happening. He starts bellowing out commands: "You soldiers of the Beast Regime, why are you afraid of these men? They don't have the Mark of the Beast, so arrest them!" He throws up his right hand and points toward Heaven as he continues shouting, "These men are false prophets, and I have permission from the Beast to have them killed. I command you to kill them right now!"

At that moment, fire shoots out of the mouth of one of the witnesses and burns off Morehead's left ear. He lets out an agonizing shriek and cries again, "Kill them!" Just as he throws up his left hand, another flash of fire shoots out and burns off his left hand; and his cries of pain fill the air.

More people in the crowd attempt to help the Beast soldiers, but one of the witnesses sends forth yet another flame of fire that kills nearly all of them as well as some more soldiers. Then with one final blast of fire, Morehead falls to the ground; and with his last breath of life, God forces him to give witness of the true God. He can't help himself from making one last agonizing confession: "I see hell waiting for me, and I know that I deserve to die and be tormented forever. I'm lost and damned for eternity! I taught people against the true God and His Holy Word, and now I'm terrified of what's to become of me. I know hell is my destiny!" Then he cries out, "Kill me! Kill me! My body is burning up inside and out!" Another flash of fire goes forth out of one of the witnesses' mouths, and Morehead is dead...and in hell he lifts up his eyes.

Luther can hardly believe what he has just seen, and he can't take any more; so he attempts to get out of there as fast as he can. He scrambles over so many dead bodies that he feels like he's in a cemetery with no graves. Mangled bodies of the Beast Regime soldiers and those who had tried to help them are strewn everywhere, and those who are still alive are frantically crying out to God for forgiveness. Many who may have never sincerely prayed before suddenly want to get right with God. Not in his wildest dreams could Luther have ever imagined such a horrific scene. Even outside the church, there are dead bodies littering the streets as far as two blocks away.

The evening news carries the whole gruesome slaughter, and Luther is glad that it also includes the final testimony that God forced through Morehead. The report states that 583 soldiers of the Beast Regime had been killed, and people couldn't get over the fact that the fire shooting out of the witnesses' mouths had caused such death and destruction...but only to those with the Mark of the Beast. The report even broadcasts every minute of Morehead's hideous death for all to see, something Luther never thought would happen.

During the next few days, Luther doesn't have to be as cautious as usual when he goes out and about because fear of the witnesses is temporarily keeping the Beast Regime soldiers off the streets. They're deathly afraid for their own safety and don't seem to be arresting people for the time being. Although Morehead was a devoted follower of the Antichrist, the Beast doesn't pay any tribute to his death because of the final confession God had forced him to make. The Antichrist considered him to be a traitor when he gave testimony of the true God of Heaven.

After that mass killing, the world fears the two witnesses sent from Heaven more than ever before; and the fear gets even greater when people realize the witnesses can also call down any kind of plague at will, which is yet another prophecy being fulfilled. **These have power to shut heaven, that it rain not in the days of their prophecy: and have power over waters to turn them to blood, and to smite the earth with all plagues, as often as they will** (Revelation 11:6).

The two witnesses strike fear in the hearts of people all over the world. Many had once thought the Beast had all power, but they're quickly learning that's not so. They also notice that the Beast is mysteriously keeping himself out of sight now that the two witnesses are killing every soldier of the Beast Regime they can find.

The soldiers continue to be more cautious and constrained for quite some time, but it doesn't last. They're so devil possessed that once the fear of the witnesses begins lifting, the devils in those soldiers manifest themselves more than ever before; and they begin torturing those who will not take the Mark beyond anything the human mind can comprehend.

Luther makes it a point to assure all those he knows without the Mark that they don't have to be afraid of the witnesses, and he points them to Revelation 11. "The witnesses are fighting for those who have not taken the Mark," Luther explains. "When they call down plagues, it means calamity for those who have the Mark; but you who haven't taken it and sold your soul to the devil have help that you're not aware of." That gives Luther and the other Christians at least one thing they can rejoice about.

Things keep getting worse for Luther; so in his desperation to get food, he comes up with a daring and dangerous plan—he's going to make a fake mark for himself. He knows that the Mark is given in the right hand; so because he's left-handed and has always been good at art, he thinks for sure that he can duplicate the Mark of the Beast if he can only find the right kind of ink. People have counterfeited money for years in America, so why can't he counterfeit the Mark?

Luther feels sure that he can counterfeit it so well that only an expert who studies it closely will be able to recognize the difference; but there is one problem—without first having the Mark, he can't buy the ink. After much thought, the only solution he can come up with is to find a way to break into a place he knows that would have the exact ink he needs...but how and when?

One night, Luther gets just the chance he

needs. A large hotel catches fire, and people from all over the city flock to it to see what's going on; so while everyone is caught up with the fire, Luther takes advantage of his perfect opportunity. The store he needs to get into is very near the hotel—so near, in fact, that the heat of the fire damages the alarm system. Luther is able to break a small side window which is out of sight of the busy street and crawl in unnoticed. He's been to this small specialty shop before, so he knows exactly what he needs and where to find it. He quickly grabs the ink, slips out of the same window and runs all the way home, looking behind him every few yards to make sure no one is following him. When he finally gets inside, he's totally out of breath but relieved that he's safe for now...or is he?

Luther goes to work right away. The ink is guaranteed to last on almost any kind of surface, so now he just has to make his art-work convincing. Luther has been carefully studying the Mark on people's faces and hands when he passes them on the street or when he gets close enough to someone who isn't paying attention to what he's doing. The image of the Mark has been burned into his mind; so with great determination and patience, he works to make his mark look just like the real thing. He knows it will have to be nearly perfect to convince store clerks, bank tellers or any other business person he needs to deal with; but he's most concerned with store clerks because he needs food more than anything else.

Luther works all night and finally duplicates the Mark of the Beast to his own satisfaction. When he looks at it, he can't tell the difference; and he feels that most other people won't be able to see the difference either. He believes his mark is just as good as the best counterfeit money ever created.

Luther is so tired from working all night that he sleeps for most of the day. It's late afternoon when he finally wakes up, and the first test for his new mark comes sooner than he had anticipated when he decides to go out and see if the Beast Regime is around. As he approaches a street corner in the main part of the city, he notices two Regime soldiers standing there. As he gets closer, he recognizes that they're captains. A cold chill runs down Luther's spine, and his legs suddenly feel like rubber; but he knows he must remain as calm and cool as he possibly can.

To make things worse, Luther knows one of the men, Jim Collins, will recognize him because he grew up with him at Fairview Church. As he walks toward them, he studies their expressions; and he tries to have the same type of expression on his face when he passes by. At first, they appear to be very threatening toward him because they don't think he has taken the Mark; but after he lets them get a glimpse of his fake mark on his hand, they change completely; and one of them says, "Luther, we didn't know you were one of us. Isn't it great that the old Bible doesn't have power over us anymore? The Beast has set us free from all of its ridiculous superstition, and I feel terrific!"

Jim pats him on the back and says, "Luther, why don't you become a soldier like us? I guarantee that you'll absolutely love being a part of the Beast Regime. I can show you exactly where to go to get your instructions, your uniform and badge and anything else you need. Then when you become an official member of this powerful army, you can help us bring in all the crazy heretics and put them to death. You'll be amazed at the tremendous satisfaction you'll find in killing these lunatics. We don't need these people here on Earth."

Luther doesn't know what to say, but he knows he has to be very careful; so he quickly says, "Thanks for the information, Guys, but can we talk about this later? I'm on my way to an appointment, and I'm already late." He walks away slowly at first and then hurries on down the street as fast as he dares, covered with cold sweat and with his heart nearly pounding out of his chest. Well, that had been his first test, and he's pretty sure neither Jim nor the other captain suspected anything; so immediately he starts thanking God Almighty from the bottom of his heart for protecting him.

Luther now figures it's pretty safe for him to try going to the supermarket to buy some groceries. He's so hungry as he pushes his cart up and down the aisles that he loads it up. He tries not to look nervous as he finally pushes his cart up to the cashier and flashes her his mark. When she gives him a big smile, he knows he has succeeded in deceiving her. He pays the bill, quickly picks up his groceries and heads for home, so thankful that he can now buy food whenever he needs to and that he won't starve to death.

After these two incidents, Luther's pretty certain that his mark will protect him from whatever he might come up against. He knows, however, that he'll have to be very careful with it when those who are in authority or counterfeit experts are around. He also knows that he can't let anyone see him delivering food to others because they'll question him and maybe even follow him, but Luther's determined not to let anything stop him from helping those in need.

Luther always takes the necessary precautions, and he becomes a great blessing to many of those who don't have the Mark whom he feels he can trust. However, Luther never tells a soul about his fake mark—he doesn't trust anyone with that secret. His friends can't figure out how he's able to get food and supplies, but they don't seem to care as long as he shares with them...and that he does.

CHAPTER
NINE

Unfortunately, Sidney Moore, one of Luther's acquaintances from the past, had gone back into the world soon after the Rapture. He had taken the Mark shortly after it was introduced; and when he reads the poster about joining the Beast Regime, he can't wait to get to Calvin Heights to register. When he arrives, quite a few men, all with the Mark as well, have already gathered. Within a few minutes, they're all ushered into a large room and seated around small tables. The speaker, Launcelot Browning, is a loud, arrogant man with two long, deep scars on his right cheek;

and his eyes glitter with demon power.

"Men," he announces, "as you have read on the posters, you have been called here for one main purpose—to help rid the world of impostors and traitors. Our aim is to rule the world under one government and to make people like it. All those who call themselves Christians or who pray to any other god besides the Beast will be arrested and given a chance to recant. Why?—because each person we can get to surrender and become one of us will make us stronger. However, we won't stand for any foolishness from anyone. Do you understand?" he snarls.

Then a slimy sneer covers his face as he continues, "There are ways to make people change their minds...or make them wish they had. No means of torture is considered too cruel for this regime. The more extreme the torture, the better it is. We want heretics to suffer as much as possible, and we'll show them no mercy. You'll be generously rewarded for all of your work; but if you let one person go free who doesn't take the Mark—even if it's a friend or a loved one—you will be put to death, no questions asked. We can't let our personal feelings hinder us from doing our work as the Beast demands it to be done, so you'd better empty yourselves of all love and sympathy for any of your friends or family who might hold out.

"Now, Men, you'll find your uniforms in the next room; and we want you to begin at once. Your first assignment is to round up everyone who doesn't have the Mark. People have had plenty of time to take it voluntarily; so now, it's time to use force! In addition to your regular salary, you'll be paid a bonus for every person you turn in. That's all for now, so go get your uniforms." Then Launcelot whirls around on his heels and leaves the room.

Sidney follows the rest of the men to the next room, and he feels so proud of himself as he puts on his new uniform. It has shiny gold buttons down the front and bright, polished ensigns of the Mark of the Beast on the cap and sleeves. A silver badge that identifies him as a member of the Beast Regime is prominently displayed on the left lapel of his coat.

After all the men are dressed, they're told to go back to the room where they had received their first orders and line up to take the oath of the Beast Regime. When all the men are in order, Launcelot Browning comes back and stands in front of them, rigidly looking straight ahead. "Attention!" he commands loudly. "Keep your eyes on the image of our god as you raise your right hand and repeat after me."

Each man solemnly and obediently does as he's commanded; and with a devilish smirk on his lips, Launcelot begins reciting the pledge; and all the men follow in unison: "'I swear by the Beast that I will do all that is within my power to rid the world of heretics, impostors and traitors. I will spill my own blood, if necessary, to convert everyone I can who prays to or worships any other god besides the Beast. If they will not accept the Beast, I will put them to death. I will show no mercy but will, with the authority vested in me, imprison and torture people until they surrender or die.'

"Lower your hands," Launcelot sternly

orders. "Now we have come to the last step." He turns, and from an ornate pitcher on a nearby table, he pours some red liquid into a golden goblet overlaid with diamonds, sapphires, jaspers and other precious stones. Then he turns back and proudly says, "This is the blood of a Christian who was killed today because he would not give up his faith in his so-called God and worship the Beast. As you pass this around, each man must take a sip; and in the name of the Beast, we pray that you will become thirsty for the blood of all Christians and sympathizers."

After this devilish act, each man receives the remaining pieces of his uniform—a gun to strap on one hip, a shiny sword for the other and a whistle on a golden chain that attaches to a buttonhole in his shirt. The new soldiers are now ready to wreak havoc and to shout the bloodcurdling cry of honor and glory to the Beast.

They hurry from the room, anxious to do the Beast's service; and they begin going from house to house, searching diligently for those who don't have the Mark and are making no effort to get it. The period of mercy determined by the Beast is over.

This new group of Beast Regime soldiers will soon have a grave effect on the lives of three young girls from Fairview Church—Violet, Sally and Purple Belle. At first, all three girls had stuck together; but as the weeks had turned into months and the months into years, they had drifted apart. The Beast had made his appearance and convinced most of the world that he was their man and that he had all the answers for anything they would need. The Antichrist was indeed fulfilling the prophecy of Daniel's little horn—he had brought prosperity to the whole world and divided the spoil. He made all kinds of riches available during those first three-and-a-half years, dividing the wealth among the people; and most of them went wild over him.

Many people had continued going to the dead churches because it was the "in thing" to do. For a while, some of them had even attended Fairview; but it had changed now because there was no one to really guide them, and most people lost interest.

After the dreadful Rapture Day, Violet had turned to God almost immediately. Purple Belle, however, couldn't seem to find the Lord for quite a long time. She had been so headstrong and disobedïent to her grandparents that she was afraid God wouldn't forgive her; but she wanted more than anything to see her grandparents again, and she knew that the only way she could do that was to get right with the Lord. Finally, the day came when she was able to humble herself enough to pray through to God's glorious salvation; and through the blood of Jesus, she was born new. She called Violet right away, and the two of them praised the Lord and rejoiced together.

Sal prayed earnestly for a while; but when she couldn't seem to find any help in the Lord, she slacked off. Because she had been such a rebellious teenager, it was then easy for her to once again take up with other young people who were wild and reckless. By this time, there was such a lack of character in most of the young people that they were doing whatever they wanted to do; and when the

Mark was introduced, Sal was so deceived
that she took it immediately. A short time
later, she joined the Beast Regime just as
Sidney Moore had.

Violet and Purple Belle never even considered taking the Mark; but of course without
it, they had no way of buying food. Luther
started helping the girls before things got too
bad by smuggling food to them at night. They
had managed that way for several months;
but when the Beast Regime started searching
the houses in their neighborhood for those
who hadn't taken the Mark, they knew it
was just a matter of time before they would
be arrested.

One afternoon, as Violet and Purple Belle
are praying together, reading the Bible and
having their own little church service, they're
rudely interrupted by a loud banging on the
front door. They hold their breath; and their
hearts almost stop when they hear a devilish
voice shout, "Open the door by the order of
the Beast Regime!" Purple Belle slowly walks
to the door and starts to open it; but before
she can get fixed, the soldiers barge right

in. It doesn't take long for them to see that Violet and Purple Belle don't have the Mark of the Beast, so they immediately arrest the two girls and take them to prison.

When they arrive, the girls are petrified. The captain of the prison notices how young and pretty Violet and Purple Belle are, so he tries in a stern yet fatherly way to convince each of them to take the Mark. They both quickly refuse, and the captain's demeanor instantly changes to one of fury. "I tried to help you," he snarls, "but since you can't be reasoned with, you'll have to face your punishment." He calls one of the soldiers and orders, "Take them to the chop block; maybe there they'll change their minds."

Violet and Purple Belle are led to the block of sure doom; and as they approach it, they're astonished to come face-to-face with Sidney Moore and Sally Morgan. "So I see that you two have decided to wise up and take the Mark," Sal mocks with a devilish sneer.

Sidney steps forward with an evil grin and says, "I know both of these girls, too. Why don't you put the one with the black hair,

Violet, in a prison cell and let her watch what happens to her friend, Purple Belle. Violet has always been more timid, so she may decide to recant and take the Mark. That other one, Purple, is pretty headstrong; I don't think we stand a chance at changing her mind."

Two soldiers grab Violet and take her to a prison cell where she will be forced to watch the horrifying torture they have planned for Purple Belle. The soldiers are determined to break Violet's spirit and convince her to take the Mark of the Beast.

One big bully shoves Violet into the cell with such force that she falls to her face on the cement floor. "Get up!" he shouts, "and get to that window before I have to get ugly!" Violet picks herself up and scrambles to the window. Violet's cell is on the second floor; so she can clearly see Purple, the swordsman and the chop block. She's trembling all over as she hangs onto the window bars. She doesn't want to watch; but she knows she must, and she can't take her eyes off of Purple as she prays, "Oh, God, please do help us."

A crowd has gathered to watch the gruesome

execution, and each person there has the Mark of the Beast. The devil-possessed sergeant in charge steps forward and viciously asks, "Young lady, why don't you come to your senses? You have such beautiful hands; but if you refuse to worship the Beast and receive the Mark, we'll have to cut off a couple of your fingers."

Purple is shaking so violently that she can hardly stand; and she's praying with all of her heart, "God, help me to stand for you."

Violet is now clinging so hard to the window bars that her fingers turn completely white; and she prays to God with all of her might, "Dear God, please be with Purple!"

The sergeant impatiently waits for Purple's response; and she finally declares loud and clear, "I will never take the Mark, and I do mean never!" The swordsman immediately cuts off two of her fingers, and she falls to the ground crying out in pain. Then it's as if some unknown strength suddenly takes her over; and she boldly proclaims, "Oh, Jesus, I love you! I know you died for me and forgave me of all my sins. Your grace is sufficient for me now and for eternity."

With that, the crowd goes wild, cursing, blaspheming and just daring her God—if there be such a being—to come down. They begin chanting like a band of demons, "Shove her teeth down her throat and shut her up. Cut her in pieces and get rid of her!"

The soldier then grabs Purple by the hair and holds her head between his hands while the swordsman cuts off both of her hands. After a brief but agonizing shriek that rings throughout the prison yard, Purple passes out. Violet knows that the merciful God has come down to Purple; and she will never feel another pain as the swordsman continues to cut off her arms and legs, then chops her body into pieces.

At this point, Violet falls from the window in a dead faint. She doesn't know how long she has been lying on the floor; but she comes to herself when the soldiers open her cell door and throw another girl inside. Then they angrily slam the door, cursing and yelling the whole time. To Violet's amazement, it's Mitzi Newhart, a girl she knows from high school. Mitzi has always been a quiet girl, very pleasant but shy. She was never what you'd call beautiful, but she always stood out because of her stunning head of thick, chestnut brown hair. She immediately throws her arms around Violet, and they both sob uncontrollably. Then Mitzi says, "Oh, Violet, I didn't know they had arrested you. Are you hurt?"

"Not yet," Violet quietly answers. "But they sure have handled me roughly. They arrested Purple and me together, but they think they can get me to take the Mark of the Beast; so they made me watch..." She stops to catch her breath as tears run down her face, "while they tortured her to death. But thank God, Purple was saved and wouldn't take the Mark, and she is now in Heaven. I can still hear her last words, 'I will never take the Mark!' I thought my heart was going to stop beating when they cut off some of her fingers; but when they cut off her hands, I felt like I couldn't even breathe. I'm so thankful that Purple passed out before the swordsman cut off her arms, legs and head and then chopped her precious body to pieces. I must have passed out after that because I don't remember anything else until they threw you in here." The tears are flowing down Violet's face like rivers; and Mitzi wraps her arms around her, rocking her and gently stroking her hair until the tears slow down, and she stops shaking.

"Oh, Violet," Mitzi pleads, "you must help me find Jesus! I know I'll be damned and thrown into the lake of fire for all eternity if I take the Mark. Please, please help me find the Lord before the guards come for me!"

With all the love and grace of God within her, Violet says, "Mitzi, Jesus will save you. He forgave me, and I'm free; and I know without a doubt that salvation can be yours, too." Mitzi begins to seek God like never before; and Violet cries out to God with her whole heart praying, "For Christ's sake, save Mitzi!" They pray for some time; and with Violet truly believing that Mitzi will be saved and born new through the divine blood that Jesus shed on Calvary, Mitzi finally lets out the glorious shout of victory that Violet has anxiously been waiting to hear. They hug each other just as if they have both already reached Heaven, and they shout and praise God.

Another precious saint of God is in the next cell, and Violet and Mitzi can hear her praising God right along with them. Although the girls can't see the woman, they begin talking with one another. She lets them know she has found Jesus; but with tears of regret, she tells them the story of how for years she had rejected the salvation that was born in Bethlehem. "My daughter, Marcie, married into a godly family," she begins. "They were all Spirit-filled and believed that Jesus was coming soon for His Bride. I tried to talk her out of marrying Coleman because I thought he and his family were fanatics; but Marcie insisted over and over, 'Mother, they're wonderful people if you would only get to know them!'

"Marcie eventually found the Lord and became Spirit-filled herself. She would always try to talk to me about the one flight out, the end-time signs and the prophecies on the coming of the Lord; and she longed for me to go to church with her...but I always refused.

"After a few years, Marcie and Coleman had a little boy whom I adored very much. He was so cute and lovable; and he asked me one day, 'Big Mama'—that's what he used to call me—'why don't you go to church?' I was really taken aback by his question, and I didn't know what to say. I finally answered him; but my heart wasn't in it when I said, 'Honey, maybe one day I will.'

"The day the Rapture took place, I woke up about eight o'clock and turned on the news. When I realized what was going on, I froze... and I could just hear my sweet daughter saying, 'Mom, the Lord Jesus is coming soon; don't wait too long.' When I finally came to my senses, I frantically tried to call her; and although I kept trying, I couldn't reach her. I knew I just had to find her; so I ran all the way to her house, which was about a half a mile away.

"When I got there, I noticed the blinds were still closed. I repeatedly pounded on the door and rang the doorbell, but no one answered.

I remembered that they always kept a key hidden under the back steps, so I ran around and grabbed it; and in my panicked state, I somehow managed to unlock the door. When I walked in, all was as silent as a tomb. I ran through the house yelling, 'Honey, are you home?' Her husband always went to work very early in the morning, so I walked into her bedroom. It looked so strange because the covers had not been disturbed on either side of the bed. I quickly threw back the quilt on my daughter's side, and only her pajamas were lying there.

"I could feel myself starting to lose it as I suddenly thought about the baby. I rushed to the nursery crying and calling, 'Buddy, Darling, are you awake?' I threw back the covers, but my little Buddy was gone. I couldn't hold back the screams any longer; and I found myself pleading, 'Come back, Jesus! Don't leave me!' But I knew it was too late. Jesus had already come.

"I began to notice a strange presence in the room; and I sank to the floor, crying and praying. After quite a while, I just knew I had to get to my daughter's church where she and her husband had always been faithful members. While I was on my way, I saw screaming, hysterical people everywhere. Some tried to stop me, frantically crying, 'My baby is missing!' or 'My little children are gone; you have to help me!' It was a nightmare! And I kept thinking, 'Surely, I'm going to wake up from this.'

"Somehow, I made my way to the church, crying, praying and blinded by tears. I stumbled in like a drunk to find the place was full of people, but thank God I managed to find a place at the altar. I stayed there crying and pleading for hours, completely unconscious of my surroundings. I didn't care who was there or what they were saying; I just knew that Jesus had come, and I was left behind because my poor, ignorant soul had been deceived. I realized what a fool I had been to have listened to the devil instead of my daughter; and after hours of begging God to forgive me, I finally found peace.

"I'm sure you girls have lived through the same nightmare that I have; and now, unless

I take the Mark, I will be tortured to death in the morning." The girls can now hear her voice trembling as she continues, "I apologize for taking up so much of your time, but it seemed I must pour out my heart to someone. I can't tell you that I'm not terrified; but I do know that whatever torture awaits me, God's grace will help me. I will never take the Mark of the Beast."

Violet speaks up at once and says, "Dear One, thank you for sharing your story, and we're so happy you found the Lord. Mitzi, the girl here in the cell with me, just found Jesus as her Lord and Savior a short while ago. That's why you heard our shouts of joy. We know we're going to be killed, too; but no matter what they do to us or how much we have to suffer, we won't bow and worship the Beast."

About that time, a nasty, foulmouthed guard curses at them and hollers, "Hey you girls in there, shut up! If I hear another sound out of you, you won't live to see the dawn!"

The conversation ends, and Violet and Mitzi fall into a deep sleep, wrapped in each other's arms. The next morning, they're abruptly awakened by a guard rattling the cell door. "Wake up, you little rats, and say goodbye to your ignorant friend next door who will die today if she doesn't take the Mark. Feel free to watch out your cell window," he sneers, "and you'll find out what will happen to you if you don't take the Mark."

As the guard leads the woman past Violet and Mitzi's cell, she quietly says, "My name is Pearl, and I have found the Pearl of great price. I will pray for you two precious girls. I love you, and Jesus loves you. I'll meet you in Heaven."

With tears in their eyes, both girls say, "Goodbye, Pearl, we will pray for you, too." Then Violet whispers, "Remember, the Lord is with you." The guard has allowed Pearl to stop and talk to the girls, hoping it will convince them to take the Mark of the Beast; but when he realizes that isn't happening, he just growls at them and shoves Pearl down the hall.

Violet and Mitzi stand together at the cell window and watch as Pearl is led to the chop block like a lamb to the slaughter; and the old, devil-possessed guard shouts, "Woman, don't be so ignorant. Come to your senses and worship the Beast. If you don't, we'll cut out your tongue!" Pearl shakes her head no, and the guard grabs her and tries to shout over the noise of the cheering crowd that has gathered saying, "Stick out your tongue!" But before he has a chance to do anything to stop her, she boldly cries out her last words in a loud voice, "The Beast is not God; he is false, and he is of the devil. I will only praise the true and Almighty God of Heaven! I have Jesus in my heart, and He is the real Savior of the world."

The guard is furious as he grabs Pearl by the throat, whips her head back and holds it while the swordsman cuts out her tongue. The blood begins gushing out of her mouth, and Violet and Mitzi are so relieved to see that Pearl has fainted. They have been praying, and they know it's finally over for her. But before they turn away from the window, they're astonished to see the glory of the Lord all around her. Devilish shouts continue to come forth from the crowd as the swordsman goes on to cut off her head, her arms and then chops her body into pieces. But none of it matters to Pearl because she has made it through to God's beautiful Heaven.

Violet and Mitzi feel like they've been to hell and back having to watch such a hideous death, but they will never forget that the Lord let them see His glory. They know Pearl is in Heaven for sure, safe forever in the arms of Jesus.

Violet and Mitzi know one of them will be next, and Violet's thoughts go to Luther and how he has helped her survive. She knows she would have been caught long ago by the Beast Regime if Luther had not kept her stocked with food and water, and she yearns to see him one more time and thank him for his kindness; but she knows that's impossible. Still, she's happy that Mitzi has found the Lord; and although the girls know their deaths will be the worst kind imaginable, they rejoice to know that it won't be much longer until they're in Heaven. They both take great consolation in knowing that Jesus is with them and that He won't forsake them.

A short time later, Violet and Mitzi hear heavy footsteps stomping down the hall; and a key turns in the lock of their cell door. A hideous-looking guard throws the door open and every nerve in the girls' bodies seems to be screaming as they wonder which one of them is about to die. "Have you two gotten over your ignorant childishness?" he growls. His face is covered with a demonic sneer that seems to curl his lips. "You girls are so stupid. You should have taken the Mark in the beginning and spared yourselves these past months of torture and near starvation."

Violet begins to break out in a cold sweat as she just stares at him with glassy eyes. He goes into a rage, grabs her by the throat and shakes her as blasphemies pour out of his mouth. "Don't tell me you still have that ridiculous belief of a Jesus who came and kidnapped people and of a God who is supposed to be up in Heaven somewhere. Do you know His name? Have you ever seen Him? I can see my god, look into his face and hear his voice. His Mark gives me a glorious feeling like nothing else I've ever felt before. I've found freedom from all of that Bible superstition that has ruined so many lives."

His tone of voice softens for a moment when he realizes that his cruelty and curse words don't seem to move either girl. "Come on, Girls," he coaxes, "you're both young and good-looking, so save your lives and take the Mark. The Beast doesn't want you to die, and I don't want to have to torture you. Get with the program, and you can walk out of here free with plenty of good food to eat and cool, clear water to drink."

The girls say nothing; so the guard starts fuming again as he gets right into Violet's face and screams, "This is your last chance; I'm running out of patience!"

Violet's tongue seems to be frozen in her mouth, but she manages to stammer, "No...I can never take the Beast's Mark; it's the Mark of eternal damnation."

With that, the guard grabs Violet by the hair and says with an evil grin, "Bring me some torture tools. It's time to have some fun." The other guard runs out and is back in no time with something that the girls soon learn will be used to pull out Violet's fingernails. One of the big, rough-looking guards grabs Violet and holds her while the other one pulls out her fingernails one by one. Her agonizing screams seem to rock the entire prison, and the pain is so excruciating that she feels she can't take another minute of it...but still, she knows she'll never take the Mark.

By this time, Mitzi is slumped over in the corner, crying hysterically; she has never witnessed anything so horrible in all of her life. A guard orders her to get up, but she's too weak to stand. Then a guard with demons dancing in his eyes grabs her up, smacks her face and pushes her down onto a disgusting, dirty, old cot and roars, "You'd better sit there while you can because soon you're going to be at that window over there to watch your ignorant friend die. Then I think you might just want to change your mind and take the Mark."

Luther has no idea what torture Violet is enduring that day or that she has even been arrested as he thinks, "Tonight, I must take

Violet some food. It's been a few days since I've last seen her, and I'm sure she's running low." It's now late afternoon; and when Luther turns on the TV to catch the latest news, he's shocked to see the announcer reporting live from the prison yard.

"You'll find tons of excitement here today," he begins, "as something sensational is about to happen. For the first time, we're going to bring you live coverage of the torture and ultimate death of some of those who refuse to take the Mark of the Beast. The two girls seen here will be the next victims, and it will all take place right here in just one hour. You definitely won't want to miss this.

"Never before have we been permitted to show these events, but the Beast Regime in this area feels that letting people see these hideous deaths will convince many young people now in hiding to come forth and take the Mark. There will be no penalty or punishment to anyone who comes out of hiding and takes the Mark today. Each person will be able to walk away totally free."

Luther fights with all the strength he has

left to keep from fainting when he sees Violet and Mitzi on the screen. He knows Mitzi, but not as well as he does Violet; and he feels so strongly that he must be there for her. He knows he will have to risk his life, but Violet will need him to be there if there is any possible way. He will have to take a great chance, but he's willing to do it.

A large crowd has already gathered when Luther arrives; and the news reporters are there in full force, pushing and shoving to get as close as possible since it's the first time they've been permitted to cover such an execution. Each news reporter stands ready with microphone in hand just waiting for the gruesome event to begin.

Since Luther has only his fake mark, he doesn't want to get too close to the cameras because if one of them gets a good shot of it, somebody might realize that his mark isn't real. As Luther inches forward, he knows he could be in for big trouble; but he wants Violet to see him so she'll know he's there and that he's praying for her. When they finally bring Violet out, he doesn't even recognize her. Her face has been beaten to a pulp, and she's disfigured far beyond anything he could have ever imagined. There's so much blood running down her face and into her eyes that she can hardly see, but she does manage to spot Luther. When she smiles at him, he knows she has recognized him.

The guard picks up Violet as if she's an animal and shouts to the crowd in a voice that sounds like it has come straight from hell, "Look, People, isn't this a beautiful sight? We've already pulled out all of her fingernails and given her a custom make-over, but that's nothing compared to what you're about to see." At that moment, the swordsman steps forward; and with one quick swipe, he cuts off one of Violet's ears and some of her fingers. Luther is sure that her agonizing cries can be heard for miles; and he has to turn away as he desperately prays, "Oh, dear God, help her! She can't stand much more!" But since Violet has put all of her love and faith in God, Luther doesn't realize how much God is already helping her.

Then, like the devil himself, the guard grabs

Violet by the hair and starts dragging her like a rag doll over to a stake that is in the form of an upside-down cross where she will be burned to death. "She has put her faith in a Cross," he sneers, "so we have brought in a very special cross just for her. Look at your cross, you foolish girl!" he orders. "You're such an idiot to give your life for nothing."

Luther is moved with such compassion that he forgets about himself and the danger he's in, and he moves in closer to Violet. Then, as if by some miracle, she sees him again and faintly smiles; and his heart leaps within him. Many people notice Violet's expression change; but thankfully, they don't realize it's because she sees Luther. Everyone's eyes are glued on Violet, and nobody is looking at him.

The guards chain Violet to the stake like she's a piece of trash; the wood is ignited, and the flames start licking up around her. As they rise higher and higher, she sends a deathly chill through the whole crowd by shouting praises to God for sending Jesus from Heaven. "Jesus is the true Savior," she shouts, "and

His Father is Lord God Almighty who has power over all!" In her final seconds, she turns her head Luther's way; and she actually looks angelic as she cries, "The victory has come! I see the gate of Heaven!"

The people in the crowd begin to hiss and shout so loudly that the sergeant on duty commands more wood to be piled up around Violet so the fire will quickly shut her mouth forever. Then just before the flames completely engulf her, she lifts up a charred, black hand; and with a voice of triumph, she victoriously shouts, "I see Jesus!" This paralyzes the crowd for a moment; but then they become like a pack of wild demons, shaking their fists and cursing Violet's God.

This brings Luther back to reality and the danger he might be in. He quickly glances over to the other side of the crowd, and he spots Sidney and Sal. They're carrying on like a couple of devils, hollering and dancing as if they've gone completely mad; and he knows he has to get out of there before they see him.

Luther moves as fast as he dares so as not

to focus attention on himself, and he finally makes it out of the crowd. He takes quite a few detours on the way home because he fears he might be followed; and when he finally gets into his house, he falls down on the couch in his living room, thanking God he has made it safely home. This day has been the worst nightmare of Luther's life, and his head throbs with such dreadful pain that it feels like it might burst wide open. He feels sick to his stomach, too weak to even move; and fear gnaws at every part of his body.

Luther can hardly look at the screen when the six o'clock news comes on because he doesn't want to see Violet's hideous death again, but he knows he will have to watch every scene carefully to make sure that no camera picked him up. He sighs with relief when he doesn't see himself at any time, thankful that the camera crews only had Violet on their minds. Her final words gave Luther great strength as he heard them again on television. He knew she had won and that no one could ever hurt her again. It encouraged Luther so much to see how frightened the people were when her voice rang out in victory. Surely, even Satan's devils all trembled at such a glorious death.

That night, Luther sleeps very little because he's tormented with one horrible nightmare after another; and he knows that Mitzi will be tortured to death in the morning. He finally dozes off in an early morning hour, but he doesn't sleep long. He soon wakes up and turns on the news just in time to see the guard who had been in charge of putting Violet to death being interviewed. "What did you think about the girl who was burned at the stake?"

"Oh, she was crazy," he growls. "She didn't know what she was saying. We definitely won't allow her friend to spew out such ignorant thoughts."

Luther decides that since he doesn't know Mitzi that well and she won't be looking for him, he won't take the risk of going to see her die; however, he does tune in that evening to see the report of it. The usual warning goes forth, "You had better take the Mark!" Then the scene switches to the crowd that had gathered that morning for Mitzi's death. Luther sees them doing wild, demonic dances, and the people are chanting praises to and glorifying the Beast: "There is none like him! He is god almighty! No other gods are as great as him. We worship the Beast! We worship the Beast!"

The people in the crowd are so devil possessed that they love watching others being tortured to death, and they can't wait for the show to begin. When two soldiers of the Beast Regime finally bring Mitzi out, the people begin shouting, "You foolish, ignorant girl, we want to see you die!" They had already shaved off Mitzi's beautiful brown hair, trying to shame her all they could. She walks out as one in a trance; and she keeps telling herself, "I will soon be with my loved ones. Thank you, Jesus, for the blood and for washing away all my sins."

Luther is amazed to see that Mitzi doesn't even seem to be conscious of the crowd. They have stopped the mad, devilish dancing and are watching in anticipation to see the girl die. The swordsman steps forward and asks one last time, "Will you recant and give up your faith in that ridiculous, so-called God of yours and worship the true god—the Beast?"

Mitzi doesn't blink an eye; and in fact, she doesn't even seem to hear him, so the swordsman goes berserk with anger and cuts off her ears. A man in the crowd grabs one of her ears and holds it up with devilish glee for all to see. Then the guards grab Mitzi and head for the chop block; but with all the glory of God that is upon her, she doesn't seem to feel any pain. Instead, she gives one last victorious shout, "Jesus, oh, precious Jesus, I'm coming home!"

A big, brutish sergeant shouts curse words and commands the swordsman to cut off her head immediately and shut her up. As the swordsman raises his sword, the people cry, "Kill her! Kill her!" And when the sword comes down, Mitzi has won. Jesus victory has come for her!

CHAPTER
TEN

The second three-and-a-half years of the Tribulation Period are now well underway; and as recorded in Revelation, chapters 8 and 9, the seven angels in Heaven start sending down judgments of destruction. God said He would use His angels to preach the Gospel to the whole world and to pour out His wrath upon the Earth. **The first angel sounded, and there followed hail and fire mingled with blood, and they were cast upon the earth: and the third part of trees was burnt up, and all green grass was burnt up** (Revelation 8:7). Stifling fear grips all those where the hail and the fire are falling because they know they could die at any time.

And the second angel sounded, and as it were a great mountain burning with fire was cast into the sea: and the third part of the sea became blood; And the third part of the creatures which were in the sea, and had life, died; and the third part of the ships were destroyed (Revelation 8:8,9). This judgment really scares Luther, and he can't believe the commentator can deliver the news of such a deadly, worldwide crisis in such a calm and straightforward way.

Someone had caught a shot of the great mountain of fire, and it was being broadcast on every network. People all over the world are able to see that incredible event as it happened. Although it looks like a horror film, they know it's real because they can see the oceans filled with blood and the beaches covered with thousands of dead fish. The reporter on the scene is wearing a mask and describes the stench as completely unbearable. The reporter goes on to say that hundreds of ships have been destroyed, but no one can seem to

answer the question on everyone's minds—
"What caused all of this?"

The news reporter comments, "We thought
it was bad several years ago when the massive tsunami killed thousands and swept away
homes and possessions, but this is far beyond
that. What in the world is happening to the
Earth? Millions of trees have been incinerated; all the grass has been torched, and
now a third part of our oceans have turned
to blood."

**And the third angel sounded, and there
fell a great star from heaven, burning as
it were a lamp, and it fell upon the third
part of the rivers, and upon the fountains
of waters; And the name of the star is
called Wormwood: and the third part
of the waters became wormwood; and
many men died of the waters, because
they were made bitter** (Revelation 8:10,11).
The warning goes forth to the whole world:
"Don't drink the water; it will kill you." But
thousands of people have already died from
drinking it, and many have no choice because
they have no way of getting safe water. The

Beast is trying to make water available; but it's not nearly enough for everyone, and it's only for those who have the Mark.

Fortunately, Luther has already stocked up on water, knowing this judgment might fall while he is still alive; but he's very selective in sharing it because if the Beast Regime finds out that he has water, they'll be on his doorstep in no time wanting to know where and how he got it.

The whole world is now in an uproar with one-third of the seas being blood and one-third of all water being deadly. There has never before been a crisis like this that's affected so many. People start killing one another just to get water; and soon, dead bodies litter the streets. The smell alone is enough to kill people, but the Beast is in no hurry to bury those who don't have the Mark. He wants to use this to scare more people into taking his Mark.

After the unimaginable death and destruction of the first three judgments, the very sound of an angel's trumpet strikes great fear in the hearts of people all over the world because they know it means another judgment will fall and shake the Earth. Everyone can hear the sound because each trumpet can be heard loud and clear in the heavens as well as all over the Earth.

And the fourth angel sounded, and the third part of the sun was smitten, and the third part of the moon, and the third part of the stars; so as the third part of them was darkened, and the day shone not for a third part of it, and the night likewise (Revelation 8:12). No one could have ever imagined such darkness; and this judgment sends people pouring frantically into the streets, scared to death and not knowing what to do. They realize that death could come to them and their families at any moment, and they're terrified and afraid to be alone.

Luther watches in total awe as God pours out His wrath on the Earth without mercy. How could the sun, the moon or the stars possibly be darkened?—only through the power of God, and Luther knows that even more of God's judgments are about to fall upon the kingdom of the Beast and all of those who have taken his Mark.

When the trumpet of the fifth angel sounds all over the world, the entire Earth begins to tremble. **And the fifth angel sounded, and I saw a star fall from heaven unto the earth: and to him was given the key of the bottomless pit** (Revelation 9:1). That falling star is visible to the whole world; and when people see it fall to the Earth, they run for their lives.

And he [the angel] **opened the bottomless pit; and there arose a smoke out of the pit, as the smoke of a great furnace; and the sun and the air were darkened by reason of the smoke of the pit. And there came out of the smoke locusts upon the earth: and unto them was given power, as the scorpions of the earth have power. And it was commanded them that they should not hurt the grass of the earth, neither any green thing, neither any tree; but only those men which have not the seal of God in their foreheads** (Revelation 9:2–4).

When Luther sees this, his heart begins to pound out of his chest. What will become of him, and when might he be killed? He knows the Bible says the Lord has sealed those who are His with a seal in their foreheads, but Luther doesn't really understand all about that seal. Could it be the seal of divine blood that Jesus spilled on Calvary so that people could be made into new creatures?

And to them it was given that they should not kill them, but that they [those who had the Mark] **should be tormented five months: and their torment was as the torment of a scorpion, when he striketh a man. And in those days shall men seek death, and shall not find it; and shall desire to die, and death shall flee from them** (Revelation 9:5,6). The stings from these terrifying beasts put many of those without God in such excruciating pain that they beg to die, trying to get out of that pain; but they can't...and Luther knows that this unbelievable torture will last for five months. Never has there been a time of such torment in the history of man on Earth—a time when no matter how hard people try to take their own lives, they can't die.

And the shapes of the locusts were like unto horses prepared unto battle; and on their heads were as it were crowns like gold, and their faces were as the faces of men. And they had hair as the hair of women [long hair]**, and their teeth were as the teeth of lions. And they had breastplates, as it were breastplates of iron; and the sound of their wings was as the sound of chariots of many horses running to battle. And they had tails like unto scorpions, and there were stings in their tails: and their power was to hurt men five months. And they had a king over them, which is the angel of the bottomless pit** (Revelation 9:7–11). Not even in their worst nightmares could people have ever imagined such hideous beasts. They're creatures of the devil, and the angry God of Heaven is using the devil's own creatures— against Satan's will—to bring five terrorizing months of judgment upon the Earth.

God's prophecies are not imaginary; they're all real. These devil-creatures have come forth from the bottomless pit itself, and God is the one who is using them to destroy the powers of the devil. These demonic creatures, along with angels of the devil who have been bound in chains of darkness for thousands of years, have been released by God; and they're raging all over the Earth. Nothing can stop them, and no one without the seal of God can escape their excruciating torture. **And the angels which kept not their first estate, but left their own habitation, he hath reserved in everlasting chains under darkness unto the judgment of the great day** (Jude 1:6).

The Lord forces these devils to bring judgment upon the Beast's own kingdom, which just proves that even devils have no choice but to obey the command of the Almighty God. He has stripped the Beast Regime of all authority and power, and even the Beast himself is powerless to stop all the judgments that the angels are freely pouring out and will continue to pour out for five months. God is making the Beast and his kingdom pay for all of the insidious torture they have inflicted on the people who wouldn't take the Mark.

This army of demonic locusts that has come straight from the pits of hell really provides the news media with some hair-raising stories, and they seem to go out of their way trying to scare people to death. They show the gruesome attacks of the locusts on all those with the Mark, and the whole world can see people running for their lives and hear their bloodcurdling screams as they're stung...but the Bible predicted all of it, and no one can escape from these beastly monsters. **They shall run like mighty men; they shall climb the wall like men of war; and they shall march every one on his ways, and they shall not break their ranks** (Joel 2:7).

People are so desperate to kill themselves that they're climbing onto the roofs of high buildings and trying to jump off because they're so tormented and totally consumed with fear, but God won't allow it. Soldiers of the Beast Regime try to cut off their heads with their own swords or to shoot themselves with their own guns; but the swords won't cut, and the guns won't fire. All they can do is injure themselves, and that just makes them suffer all the more.

People know that all of these judgments

and the great anguish they're causing are not coming from the Beast but from the One who sits on the throne in Heaven. God used to love all people, but now He hates those with the Mark; so no judgment is too harsh, and no suffering is too great.

As the judgments continue to be poured out, Luther once again finds himself in desperate need of food; so he carefully ventures out. People have been shut up in their houses for days, frightened beyond words; and Luther has remained shut away most of the time as well. Now, as he hurries down the street, men beg him to kill them; and soldiers desperately plead with him to take their swords and cut off their heads. As he turns a corner, he's startled by a familiar yet demonic voice screaming his name. He turns and is shocked to see Sidney Moore shouting, "Luther, get over here right now and help me!"

Luther cautiously approaches Sidney who is lying on the ground half-dead and gripping his sword; and through parched, swollen lips, Sidney weakly gasps, "Where have you been, Luther? I haven't seen you since the first day we saw our great god on TV." He winces in great pain as he continues, "I've been stung by one of those damnable creatures that are ravaging the Earth, and you just have to help me." His body starts going into mini-convulsions as he says, "I know you have the Mark and that you're one of us, so take my sword and kill me right now. When one of these creatures soon stings you, you'll see what it's like not to be able to take your life. I didn't know that one human being could suffer such horrible pain and torment. It has to be worse than hell itself because my whole body feels like it's on fire!"

Sidney moans in agony, and Luther wants more than anything to turn and run from him as fast as he can; but his legs suddenly feel like rubber, and he feels as if he's in a slow-motion nightmare. He knows that danger lurks all around him, but he can't seem to move; and even if he could, it's too danger-ous for him to run.

"Luther," Sidney stammers, "we were such close buddies for years, so have pity on me and end this suffering. I can't take it anymore!" Sidney's bloodshot eyes roll back into his head, and he's as pale as death. Not in his wildest dreams has Luther ever imagined finding Sidney in such a pitiful condition.

Luther actually starts to feel sorry for him for the moment; but when Sidney finds the strength to speak again, he spews out, "I hate the false God of Heaven! I took the Mark to spite Him and to let Him know that I would hate and despise Him forever for stealing my wife and boy from me." Luther doesn't feel sorry anymore as blasphemies continue to pour from his wretched, devil-possessed soul until he abruptly stops, looks at Luther and says, "I'm glad you showed Him how you feel, too. Now, put me out of my unbearable misery; I can't stand it anymore!"

Luther stands there speechless; but he finally manages to quietly say, "I can't kill you, Sidney. I just can't do it." Luther still can't seem to move, but somehow he gets enough strength to slowly start backing away. Sidney begins cursing and shouting, "You ungrateful fool!" So Luther uses every last bit of strength he can muster to turn and get as far away from him as he can. Sidney continues shouting until he knows Luther can no longer hear him.

Luther tries to keep moving, but he's so sick and weak that he feels like he could vomit at any minute. He knows he must be deathly ill; and when he makes his way to a bus stop, he slumps down on one of the benches with his head between his knees. He tries to pray, but he can't seem to even put two words together; and his mind is being bombarded with tormenting thoughts of, "One flight out...and I could have been on board when Jesus came for His holy saints. I knew there would be just one flight, but I never thought it would come so soon; and I never dreamed I would miss it." Luther then begins to think of his wife and twin boys, and he's so grateful that they made it out and didn't have to endure what he's going through.

Luther soon becomes so nauseated that his body begins shaking and chills shoot up and down his spine. He has a very high fever; and as he struggles to get up from the bench, he passes out. When he starts to regain consciousness, he hears a voice moaning in great despair; and he discovers it's his own. Then he feels a warm tongue on his face, and he opens his eyes to see a big but friendly-looking black dog standing over him. As Luther looks at him, the dog begins to wag his tail; and he reaches out to pat him on the head.

It feels so good to have love at a time like this, even if it is from a strange dog; but little does Luther know that the dog's owner has recently been put to death for refusing to take the Mark. Now, the big guy is just as lonely as Luther is and looking for some attention; and Luther enjoys feeling the warm touch of anything that is still living, harmless and loving.

Luther starts to feel a little better, so he slowly sits up and tries to get moving. When he's finally able to get to his feet, he looks cautiously around and then starts for home because it's getting late. After walking just a short distance, Luther notices that even though the dog is following close by, he seems tired; and his nose is checking out every nook and cranny along the way, looking for something to eat. Luther then remembers the sandwich he had shoved into his jacket pocket earlier, and he stops and pulls it out. The dog licks his mouth and looks hopefully at Luther; so with a childlike grin, Luther breaks off a piece and offers it to him, remembering the Bible story about the crumbs being eaten by the dogs. Instantly, the dog's tail starts to wag, and then his entire body seems to sway in appreciation. Luther's smile gets bigger and bigger until he can't help chuckling to himself as his new friend finishes the whole sandwich and even licks the paper that it was wrapped in. The dog has won Luther's heart, so he pats his leg with his hand as an invitation for the dog to accompany him and then steps up his pace toward home.

Before they get very far, Luther is brought back to the reality of the danger lurking all around him when he hears another voice calling his name. He freezes for a moment thinking, "What if it's someone who has been watching my comings and goings and suspects that I might not really have the Mark?"

Luther has grown accustomed to walking with his right hand about half closed so a trained eye can't study his mark.

Luther looks around and then walks cautiously in the direction of the voice without getting too close. The man's voice cries, "Luther, I need you"; but he doesn't recognize the voice and decides not to stop. "I just won't look," he thinks. "I'll just move on as if I don't hear him." But then he changes his mind thinking, "I had better not; he knows who I am." As Luther turns back, a cold chill runs down his spine; and he starts trembling like a leaf. Then perspiration breaks out all over his body like big raindrops as he realizes it's Jim Collins. He looks awful; and Luther slowly stammers, "Jim, what's wrong with you?"

Jim answers in a weak, halting voice, "One of those damnable monster locusts has stung me, and I'm in such unbelievable pain and torment that I don't want to live another minute." He squeezes his eyes shut as he tries to take a shallow breath before he says, "But I can't die. I've tried everything I can think of to kill myself, but I can't do it. You have to kill me, Luther! I order you to pick up my sword that's lying over there in the grass and do exactly as you're told."

Jim Collins is a big captain in the Beast Regime, and he's used to people obeying him. Those who don't obey make him crazy-mad, and that's exactly what happens when Luther refuses to kill him. Jim goes into a fit of insane rage and rants and raves like a madman.

Jim was the son of a dear saint of God, Mother Collins, who had loved him so much. She had warned Jim again and again that the Rapture would soon take place, but he had always ignored her warnings...and now, he had taken the Mark and damned his soul for all eternity. Precious Mother Collins' many prayers would never be answered for her beloved son.

Luther does all he can to fight off the cold, calculating voice of hell as he tells Jim, "You don't want your life to end like this; I'm sure you'll get better."

That comment seems to stir every devil in

Jim as he yells even louder, "Kill me! I feel like I'm on fire! My whole body is burning inside and out, and I can't stand it anymore! I'll gladly welcome death as a friend right now, not an enemy. I've known you nearly all of your life, Luther, so have mercy on me and help me right now; you must!" Luther can't take any more; so he turns and actually starts running while Jim continues to scream, "Come back! I want to die, and I can't do it myself!"

Luther runs as fast as he can up a back road with the dog at his heels. Death pounds in his brain as he cries to himself, "Oh, my God, how much more must I take? How much longer do I have?" Luther and the dog, which he has decided to call King, suddenly stop dead in their tracks as one of the dreadful locust beasts appears just ahead of them. Luther has never had a nightmare that comes anywhere near the sight of this locust. It's ghastly-looking with a gold crown on its head, a face like a man, long hair like a woman, teeth like a lion and a long, powerful tail with a sting in it. Luther is paralyzed with fear and can't move; and even King is too horrified to bark, although he does let out a low growl. Luther wants to get away, but he can't. Will this creature sting him? If it does, what will happen to him? Will he end up lying in the street like Jim crying, "Kill me; kill me?" He stands there stiff as a board just as if he's nailed to the ground with his heart pounding out of his chest. When he finally feels like he just can't take another minute, he cries out, "Oh, God, help me!"

Just then, the deadly creature spreads its mighty wings; and with a noise like that of a whirling tornado, it flies away. Luther feels like he's losing his mind, and he has no idea how he and King finally managed to get home that night.

Luther sprawls out on the floor in a semi-conscious state with King by his side, and darkness totally engulfs him. He has always been healthy and strong, but his body now feels like it's on fire through and through; and he has virtually no strength at all. He's running a very high fever, and that sends him into tormenting nightmares in which he feels as if he's being helplessly tossed about by the waves of the sea. Then he feels himself being stung again and again by those horrible creatures, and he just wants to die; but he can't find death anywhere as he hears a voice in his head saying, **And in those days shall men seek death, and shall not find it; and shall desire to die, and death shall flee from them** (Revelation 9:6). "I will find death," he shouts as he cries the cry of the damned. Luther's own bone-chilling screams wake him up, and he realizes he's been having a nightmare; but he's never before had a nightmare like that one—one in which he desperately wanted to die but couldn't.

Just when things seem like they can't get any worse, the sixth angel's trumpet sounds. **And the sixth angel sounded, and I heard a voice from the four horns of the golden altar which is before God, Saying to the sixth angel which had the trumpet, Loose the four angels** [These are fallen angels who have been held in chains of darkness since the devil and his angels were kicked out of Heaven.] **which are bound in the great**

river Euphrates. And the four angels were
loosed, which were prepared for an hour,
and a day, and a month, and a year, for to
slay the third part of men. And the number of the army of the horsemen [devils]
were two hundred thousand thousand [or
200 million]: and I heard the number of
them (Revelation 9:13–16). Instantly, millions and millions of demonic horsemen cover
the whole Earth, and their mission is to kill
a third part of all the billions of people who
were on Earth when the Tribulation Period
first started. This is not an army of 200 million human horsemen; they're horrifying,
demonic-looking creatures from the very
pits of darkness. The world has never seen
anything like them.

  And thus I saw the horses in the vision,
and them that sat on them, having breastplates of fire, and of jacinth, and brimstone: and the heads of the horses were as
the heads of lions; and out of their mouths
issued fire and smoke and brimstone. By
these three was the third part of men
killed, by the fire, and by the smoke, and

by the brimstone, which issued out of their
mouths. For their power is in their mouth,
and in their tails: for their tails were like
unto serpents, and had heads, and with
them they do hurt (Revelation 9:17–19).
This army of monster-like creatures kills
people with what comes out of their mouths
and with their formidable tails just as the
Lord said they would.

One day when Luther is out, he sees one of
these hideous beasts for the first time; and
every nerve in his body seems to cry out. He
has studied them in the Bible, but to actually
see them terrorizing the people of the Earth
is almost more than he can take.

It's inconceivable to Luther that such repulsive beasts could even exist, and he just wants
to run and to keep on running and never stop;
but where can he go? He runs into a building, but he doesn't feel safe there; so when
he notices a large glass window on the back
wall, he breaks the window and climbs out...
and King stays right with him. They run as
fast as they can down a back alley, passing
people left and right who are crying for help;

but Luther isn't about to stop and help anyone this time.

When Luther finally slows down, he's numb through and through. His mouth is parched, his lips are clammy, and he's shaking all over. "If fear alone could kill you," he thinks, "then I should be dead." The numbers of horsemen seem to be increasing, and panic-stricken people are frantically running in all directions. He watches the devilish tormentors overtake some of them, and he sees the fire shoot out of their mouths.

When Luther first witnesses an actual killing, he feels as if he's having a heart attack. He watches in sheer terror as poisonous smoke issues from a lion-headed horse and kills its victim instantly. There's no safety anywhere, and Luther's mind immediately goes back to the scripture in which God said a third part of the men on Earth would be killed by these creatures and that they would accomplish this in a little more than a year's time. It's no wonder the Spirit had tried to warn people again and again about the great Tribulation Period they would face if they missed the one flight out!

God is the one who is calling for the judgment plagues that are now terrorizing the inhabitants of the Earth just like He did in Moses' day when He rained the plagues down on the Egyptians. God didn't use an army to deliver the Israelites from bondage; He sent judgments through His own supernatural powers. Likewise, in the book of Revelation, He foretold that He would use angels to preach the Gospel and to rain down judgments; and He is doing just that.

Luther has studied the book of Revelation so much, and it has now become living reality to him; all of the deadly, horrifying judgments from an angry God are in action. He can just hear an angel proclaiming, "Woe, woe to the inhabitants of the Earth!" With a drawn face and haunted eyes, a weak and exhausted Luther winds his way through back alleys and finally reaches home. He breathes a sigh of relief to have not seen another sign of the horrible creatures.

Luther feels as if he has just lived through the worst nightmare possible—he had expected one of those horrible creatures to overtake him at any time. As the tension in his body begins to ease somewhat, tears start streaming down his face as he pleads and cries, "Oh, God, please help me! There's no way out of this never-ending nightmare!" Then he completely falls apart, and he just can't seem to stop crying. How much more can he take?

Luther's world has been totally destroyed, but he knows that somehow he'll have to go on. He would now welcome death, but he knows he can't commit suicide or he'd go to hell. It's hard for Luther to believe, but he knows that eternal hell would still be much worse.

Luther turns on the evening news. He never misses a day because he has to know what's going on for his own safety's sake. In the past, Barry had often joined him; and Luther would always look forward to those times because it was so nice to be able to talk to another human being about what was happening in the world. However, after Luther had created his fake mark, he knew it would no longer be safe for him and Barry to be seen together. He didn't dare tell Barry he had made a fake mark, so he just told him it would be safer for them if they didn't get together anymore. However, since Luther always seems to have plenty of food and water, Barry does stop by at night from time to time to pick up food and supplies.

At those times, they like to talk about the two witnesses who are still destroying entire armies of the Beast Regime. Armies from all over the world have joined forces to try to destroy them; but for three-and-a-half years, it's impossible to kill God's two witnesses. Instead, the two men from Heaven easily kill all of the soldiers of the Beast Regime who come against them. This really encourages those who have not taken the Mark.

Luther and Barry also discuss the black market. After the Mark of the Beast was introduced, some of those who had taken the Mark formed an underground black market. During the first three-and-a-half years of the Tribulation Period, many people who planned to never take the Mark had removed all of their savings from the banks and closed their investment accounts knowing the time would come when they wouldn't have access to any of it. They wanted to make sure they would have money to buy from those who ran the underground black market.

The soldiers in the Beast Regime always received the very best benefits from the Beast while all those who were not a part of the Regime had to do the best they could to get by. As a result, even many people with the Mark went underground and sold things on the black market; and they would sell to anyone who wanted to buy, whether they had the Mark or not. Those with the Mark didn't love or care about anyone; they just knew they needed money, and they didn't care how they got it. Even after they had established their underground businesses, they wanted to keep their customers; so they weren't about to report anyone to the Beast Regime.

Oddly enough, the Antichrist allows the news media to freely show the two witnesses doing what he calls their "dirty work"—destroying the soldiers of the Beast Regime and all those who have the Mark. The Beast hopes the soldiers will figure out how to defeat them by watching how they kill others.

During one of Luther and Barry's conversations, Barry tells Luther how the Beast Regime had sent out six soldiers to arrest a family of seven, all of whom did not have the Mark. "I watched from across the street as the soldiers were taking them out of their home," Barry sadly explains, "when all of a sudden, the two witnesses appeared out of nowhere. The soldiers were brutally beating some of the family members; and one of the witnesses shouted in a voice loud enough for all to hear, 'Get your hands off of them!'

"One of the soldiers who was evidently new thought he was high and mighty enough to kill the witness, so he threw a dagger at him. Instantly, fire shot out of the mouth of the witness and killed all six soldiers; and the family was spared from a certain hideous death.

"More recently," Barry continues, "and perhaps you saw this story on the news, members of the Beast Regime thought that many people who had not taken the Mark were hiding in a particular three-story building. About fifty soldiers surrounded the building, but little did they know that only the two witnesses were inside waiting for them. When the soldiers started shooting into the building, the witnesses jumped out from the second floor and killed every one of them with fire." Luther had definitely seen that story, too; and he was as amazed over it as Barry was.

Luther had heard another story about the Beast Regime stepping up their efforts to kill people who had refused to take the Mark. "They were evidently hoping to kill and arrest more people than ever before by banding themselves together with Regime armies in other countries," Luther recalls, "but it all turned out to be a big smoke screen because they really just wanted to try to kill the two witnesses...and that didn't happen. Instead, the witnesses appeared in the midst of all those soldiers and destroyed every one of them. The reporter on the scene said he had never seen anything like it.

"Barry, isn't it fascinating how the two

witnesses can preach to people all over the world at the same time, and everyone can hear them? The true Gospel of Jesus is being preached to all whether they want to hear it or not. It's even more amazing to hear not only the two witnesses but also many angels preaching that all must be born again through the blood of Jesus Christ, the Son of the living God. They're warning people not to take the Mark or they'll be damned for all eternity with no chance of forgiveness."

After several years, the two witnesses succeed in killing multitudes of soldiers from the Beast Regime as well as many other people with the Mark of the Beast. In fact, so many soldiers are being killed that men have become afraid to join the Beast Regime. The fire-breathing witnesses are destroying them left and right and are calling down plagues of all kinds on the soldiers and those with the Mark.

The witnesses from Heaven have no fear because they know that Lord God Almighty is their source of strength and power, and the soldiers of the Beast Regime are quickly losing their confidence. They had thought that joining the Regime would give them all the power and authority they could ever want, but they soon discover that isn't so. The two witnesses have greater power and authority than any men on Earth.

It definitely strengthens the faith of many who have refused to take the Mark to see the greatness of God's power working on Earth. The witnesses don't hide or only come out at night; they can appear at any time and anywhere, so Luther and Barry love to go and watch them in action as they use God's great, mighty power to terrorize and destroy people. However, they can only go out together at night; they can't afford to take such a chance in daylight hours.

Whenever they have the opportunity to hear the holy preaching of the witnesses as they proclaim nothing but the truth, it thrills them beyond words. The witnesses always make it plain to people that if they take the Mark, they will be damned forever; and the cup of God's indignation will be poured out upon them. The angels of God have also joined the two witnesses as preachers of righteousness and are shaking the whole Earth. They fly all over the world declaring, "Jesus Christ is the only Savior of the world!" Never in the history of man has there been anything like it. The entire world is their pulpit, and the devil can't stop them. The witnesses and the angels are indestructible!

CHAPTER
ELEVEN

Barry's parents did not serve the Lord, so they were left when the Rapture took place just as he was. He had gone to see them right after it happened, but he hasn't talked to them since then. At the time, they appeared to be crying and praying; but Barry didn't have much sympathy for them. They had been sinful people of the world who hadn't gone to church and weren't interested in hearing the Gospel of Jesus Christ.

Barry had gone to church when he was a youngster, but his parents never went with him; and they really didn't want him to go either. They loved to go to wild parties on Saturday nights, and they would never get home until the wee hours of the morning. The only reason they let Barry go to church on Sundays was to get him out of the house so they could sleep as late as they wanted to.

Barry felt it was his parents' fault that he had missed the one flight out, and he resented them for it.

That's why when he found them crying and praying right after they were left, he got very angry. He yelled at them and told them that if they had served God and gone to church like other moms and dads did, they could have all made the Rapture. Then he had stormed out and never returned.

Since that time, so much has happened—one of the most important things being that Barry has found the Lord. Now, after more than six years, Barry begins to think about his parents. He knows that, in spite of them, his lovely wife, Polly, and their three daughters had made the one flight out; so he starts thinking that he might have been too hard on his parents. His wife had tried so hard to convince him to go to church and serve the Lord, and he had promised her before they were married that he would; but he never kept his promise.

Although he hadn't admitted it at first, he now knows that it really wasn't his parents' fault that he had missed the Rapture; so one day, he decides to go and see them. Barry's nervous and his heart is pounding when he steps up to the front door and walks inside the old place he used to call home. He's relieved and starts to relax when he finds that his mom and dad are overjoyed to see their only son, and they talk together for quite some time. Barry is very thankful that his parents haven't taken the Mark, and they admit that the only reason they've survived so far is because they had taken all their money out of the bank before the Mark was enforced. They have been able to buy what they have needed through the black market. One of their greatest concerns is that, although they've continued to pray, they haven't yet been able to find salvation. "Barry, are you saved?" his mother asks anxiously.

"Oh, yes, Mom," he thankfully answers. "I have found Jesus as my personal Savior; and I know without a doubt that if we'll all pray together, the Lord will forgive you, too. I have continued going to Fairview Church, and I've learned so much." Barry takes out his little New Testament that Sadie Moore had given to him when he was just a boy, and he reads many scriptures about being born new. He talks to them about the new and living way that Jesus brought and tells them that Jesus is the only real Christ who died for all. As they both listen to him, they begin to cry tears of godly sorrow; and Barry knows they're ready to pray. He leads them in the sinners' prayer, and they repeat it with all of their hearts. When they finish, they begin to laugh and shout; and Barry is so excited. What a blessed time his visit with them has turned out to be.

Barry encourages his parents to continue praising God and reading the Holy Scriptures; and as he turns to leave, his mom begs him to stay just a little longer. She wants to make him his favorite meal. Barry can't pass up such an invitation; and besides, it's been a long time since he's had or enjoyed a decent meal with anyone. The three of them have a wonderful time together, and all of Barry's hate and bitterness toward them turns to love and forgiveness.

Barry can hardly contain himself; so on his way home, he decides to stop and see Luther. Since it's dark, he feels fairly safe in going; and it's been a good while since he's seen Luther anyway. Unfortunately, Luther isn't home; and Barry knows he has to move on because it's getting late.

About a week later, Barry decides to visit his parents again to see how they're getting along with their new-found salvation; but little does he know that someone had recognized him when he was there earlier and had reported him to the Beast Regime. Soldiers had been secretly watching his parents' house for several days; so shortly after he arrives, two Regime soldiers as nasty as the devil himself tear down the front door and force their way in.

Barry instantly jumps up and says, "Take

me; I'm ready." But one of the guards snarls back, "We're here for all three of you; and if you don't take the Mark, you'll all die a hideous death!"

Barry now loves his parents so much, and he wants the soldiers to leave them alone; but no amount of pleading will make that happen. Finally, Barry musters all the determination he can to declare, "We will never take the Mark of the Beast; we know and serve the only true God."

Barry's parents immediately chime in to agree proclaiming, "Yes, we do!" The soldiers curse under their breath and quickly handcuff all three of them, and they even beat them at times while on the way to the prison.

When they arrive, guards put Barry's mother and dad in a cell on the first floor of the prison and take Barry up to a cell on the second floor so he'll have a clear view of the torture block. When Barry first looks out the cell window, he's overwhelmed with grief because he knows many people have already died there. As usual, a large number of people have gathered in the prison yard to see more of the prisoners die; and he stares at all of them in sickened amazement wondering how people can be so devil-possessed that they enjoy watching others being tortured to death.

As he studies the crowd, he spots Sidney Moore and Sal Morgan. They had heard that Barry and his parents were arrested; so when they see him looking out the window, they start taunting, "Hey, Barry, how are you feeling? Are you ready to take the Mark? If not, we have the perfect kind of convincing for a guy like you!"

Barry quickly ducks down for a few minutes; and when he tries to peek out again, they pepper him with handfuls of gravel that sting his face. As soon as Barry ducks down the second time, he hears a familiar voice that sounds just like Heaven to him say, "You two had better not throw another piece of gravel at that precious child of God!" Barry quickly scrambles back to the window because he just knows that the witnesses from Heaven have arrived.

He sees Sal furiously turn and glare at the

two men while shouting, "Shut your filthy, dirty mouth!" Then she picks up a handful of gravel and throws it at them. At that moment, Sidney lets out a loud, devilish screech and starts throwing gravel as well; but fire immediately shoots out of the mouths of the two witnesses and instantly torches both Sal and Sidney.

The power the two witnesses have never ceases to amaze Barry; and this appearance gives him such relief, letting him know that Jesus really is with him. Then Barry begins to pray for his mom and dad because he knows they'll soon be in Heaven with his wonderful wife and three children if they'll just stay true to God. He continues to cry out to God not only for them but also for himself, praying that they'll all be strong and not take the Mark.

Barry can't sleep at all that night; he only tosses and turns. Then early the next morning, just as he had suspected, he looks out the window to see the soldiers taking his mother and dad to be tortured. He no longer cares what people do to him; so he calls down to them, "Remember, Mom and Dad, Jesus said, **I am the resurrection, and the life: he that believeth in me, though he were dead, yet shall he live** (John 11:25). That means you'll live for all eternity. I love you, and I'll see you in Heaven!"

Barry's parents throw him a kiss and holler back, "We love you, too, Son!"

The guards had already decided to kill Barry's mother quickly because they remember what the two witnesses had done to Sidney and Sal just the day before. They're also well aware that the witnesses have already killed multitudes, so they're scared stiff. Because of that, the guards aren't as pompous as usual; and on this morning, they're actually shaking with uncontrollable fear. They keep nervously looking around as if they're expecting the witnesses to show up at any time and kill them. Even the swordsman's hands are shaking when he says, "Woman, will you take the Mark and save your life?"

She boldly answers loud enough so Barry and the entire crowd that has gathered can hear her, "No, I will never give up Jesus.

He's the true Son of God, my Savior and Lord forever!"

The swordsman goes into a demonic fit of rage and cries, "Put her on the block; there's no point in fooling with her any longer!" They quickly lay her on the block; and in a split second, the scared-stiff swordsman cuts off her head. She is in Heaven at last.

The guard then turns to Mr. Gilmore and thunders in a damnable voice, "All right, you foolish man, will you give up your false God and take the Mark?"

He looks the swordsman straight in the eye and emphatically states, "No, I will not!"

The swordsman screams, "Quick, put him on the block before those crazy witnesses show up again!"

Then Barry's dad proudly shouts his last words, "I love you, Son. I have found Jesus, and all Heaven is mine!" With that, the swordsman cuts off his head. Barry can hardly see through all of his tears, but he praises the Lord that his parents didn't have to suffer much and that they're both safely home with the Lord.

Then just as he begins to turn away from the window, the torturers' greatest fear becomes reality when the two witnesses suddenly appear. Barry's glued to the window once again as he watches the swordsman throw down the bloody sword and run for his life. The other guards and all those in the crowd with the Mark scatter like ants while Barry starts shouting at the top of his lungs, "Jesus died for me and my family!" He doesn't care who hears him; and he wants the whole world to know that he'll soon be in Heaven with Polly, his three girls and his mom and dad.

Later that evening, Luther tunes in to the evening news; and his blood freezes in his veins when he hears of the Gilmores' deaths; and when they announce that the Gilmores' son, Barry, will be next, he just wants to die himself. The commentator goes on to recount how the two witnesses had showed up and killed two of their best soldiers, Captain Sidney Moore and Sal Morgan. Luther doesn't feel bad about that because of what they had become; and, in fact, he's actually glad they died. However, he is concerned about when

Barry will die.

Luther calls the TV station; and in a cruel, heartless voice, he asks when that no-good Barry Gilmore is scheduled to die. "We don't know yet," is the response. "There haven't been any deaths for three days because the guards are so afraid of the two witnesses. Supposedly, the swordsman who killed the last two people took off that day, and he's not been seen since. Some people say the two witnesses killed him. We don't know if that's true or not, but other guards are missing, too."

Luther knows it's dangerous for him to go anywhere near the prison; but he and Barry have been as close as two loving brothers, so he feels that he just has to be there when he's killed. Luther stays tuned to the news for the next few days to hear the announcement of Barry's death; and after three days, the announcement finally comes. Since the witnesses caused such chaos when Barry's parents were killed, the Regime has scheduled many extra soldiers to be on hand for Barry's execution. This is not good news for Luther, but he knows that he still has to go.

Luther's heart is so heavy; and at times, he feels like he's losing his mind. He thinks about King, his new friend, and what will happen to him if he gets caught. Still, he knows he has to go, so he puts out some food and water and leaves the door partly open so King can get out if he needs to.

Luther's standing in the crowd when they bring Barry out. Those with the Mark curse and jeer as they push and shove to get as close as they can. This gives Luther a great opportunity to press up against Barry when he passes him and whisper, "Jesus will help you; I'll see you in Glory." Barry doesn't want to give Luther away, so he just flashes a faint smile while still looking straight ahead to let Luther know he heard him.

The guards don't waste time with these executions anymore because they're afraid of the witnesses; so right away, the swordsman demands, "Will you take the Mark? If not, I'll cut you to pieces!"

Without hesitation, Barry declares, "I'm going to Heaven to see my wife and three daughters. They were on the one flight out which really did happen. Since then, I have found the real Jesus who died for me; and I will soon be in Heaven with those I love!"

The crowd goes wild with more cursing and blaspheming; then without any warning, three gunshots ring out, and Barry is dead—someone in the crowd had killed him.

Luther and the rest of the crowd are stunned. The swordsman still puts his body on the block and proceeds to chop it to pieces, but Barry is already in Heaven and doesn't feel a thing. Luther begins to slowly make his way out of the crowd, always careful to flash his fake mark. He still can't believe that nobody has yet detected it, but he doesn't really care anymore because Barry is now gone.

As soon as Luther gets out of sight of the crowd, he runs home as fast as he can; and when he gets there, King starts jumping up and down and happily wagging his tail. He seems to sense what has just happened; and although Luther is amazed, he's grateful for the attention.

Barry's death had happened so fast, and

Luther's relieved that the Regime had not been able to torture him. Then he actually smiles as he pictures Barry being reunited with his wife and three children whom he loved so dearly, and he can't wait to see his own family.

Luther can't shake the feeling that he'll soon be arrested; and because he doesn't want anything to happen to King, whom he has grown to love so much, he tries to figure out what to do with him as well as with all the money he still has left. He finally thinks of a guy, Langford Overcash, whom he believes he can trust to use the money for good and who will continue to buy food from the underground black market for others. Luther has talked to Langford on several occasions, and he knows all about the black market; so Luther decides to get in touch with him.

Just as he's about to call him, there's a knock at the door. He opens it, and he can hardly believe his eyes when he sees Langford standing there. They shake hands; and then Langford says, "For some reason, I felt I should stop by and see you today. I know you and Barry were such close friends, and I'm so sorry to hear about his death."

"I really appreciate that," Luther says, "and actually, I was just about to call you; so come on in. I have an idea I'd like to run past you since you know so much about the underground black market." Langford walks in and Luther continues, "I have a feeling that I may not be able to avoid the Regime much longer, and I have a lot of cash left that I would like to give you. You can feel free to use it to buy food for yourself, but I really need you to continue taking care of some others I've been helping along the way; I can give you a list of their names. Also, I wonder if you'd be willing to take King, my dog. I know that might be asking too much; but I can't stand the thought of him being left alone, and you can use the money I give you to buy food for him, too."

Luther is so happy when Langford agrees to do it all, and he gets the leftover money and carefully wraps it in a paper bag for Langford.

"Do you want me to take King now?" Langford asks.

"I really hate to say goodbye to him," Luther says as he snaps a leash on King's collar and gives him a loving pat, "but I think that would be best. Since the Regime has killed Barry, I know it's just a matter of time before they come looking for me."

Langford stands up, gives Luther a warm embrace and says, "I'll be praying for you, and I'll be sure to take good care of your pal." He picks up the money and turns to go, but King won't move. Luther gently nudges King until he finally stands up and slowly follows Langford out the door.

Luther can hardly bear to watch King leave because he's been such a blessing to him, and his eyes well up with tears as Langford leads the dog away; but Luther's relieved that he's found a good Christian home for him.

Just a few days later, Luther's fear comes true. While he's at home one afternoon, two members of the Beast Regime come pounding on his door. Luther takes a deep breath, swallows hard and then finally opens the door.

At this point, they think that Luther has the Mark; so they just tell him, "Our captain wants to see you." They never speak another word to him; they just force him into their truck and take him away. When Luther arrives at the prison, he's introduced to Captain Lindon Shaw.

Luther begins to introduce himself; but the captain rudely interrupts him saying, "I know your name, Luther, and no doubt you're wondering why I've brought you here. Well, the truth is that I have a few questions for you. First of all, why don't you ever do any work for the Beast Regime? A guy like you would make a good guard and perhaps even a good captain. One of our best captains, Jim Collins, has told me a little bit about you; so I've decided to keep you here for a few days and let you think it over. We could definitely use you because so many of our men have been killed by those two ferocious witnesses. Boy, would I like to give them what they deserve. My men are terrified of them. Now, I have a nice room for you on this floor. It's not a prison cell, mind you, and you'll be comfortable there; but you can't leave right now. Your meals will be served to you in your room, and I hope you'll agree to my proposition."

Luther's lips suddenly feel numb, and his tongue seems to be frozen in his mouth; but he finally mutters, "Do I really have a choice?" A devilish grin spreads over the captain's face, and he walks out.

Luther spends a couple of anxious days and restless nights there; and with each day that goes by, his counterfeit mark bothers him more and more. What should he do? He knows that if they ever find out the truth about his mark and that he's really a Christian, it'll be hell on Earth for him. In fact, he knows they'll go completely devil-crazy when they realize he's tricked them for all this time; but Luther finally decides it's time to get rid of his mark. Now, he just has to figure out how.

After a few days, he hears an announcement about a special Beast Regime meeting that all of the guards are required to attend. Luther realizes that this will probably be his only chance to try to slip out and go to a nearby store to get the special ink remover he needs. Since he isn't actually in a locked cell, once all of the guards are in the meeting, he sneaks out a back door unnoticed. He stays hidden in the shadows and avoids all lights as he runs to the store as fast as he can, praising the Lord for protecting him all the way there. Once inside, he's relieved to see that there are no customers, just one clerk. He has run so fast that he can scarcely get his breath, but he manages to tell the clerk what he wants.

On his way back to the prison, Luther has an overwhelming urge to flee. Why, this is his big chance to not have to go back and face certain death. But just as he turns to run the other way, he thinks of Barry and Violet who had died such victorious deaths without fear. He longs to see his wife, Bobbie, and their precious twins, and he admits to himself that life just isn't worth living anymore without them. Also, he knows that it would be just a matter of time before he would be caught again. So with a made-up mind and a prayer in his heart, he makes his way back to the prison, thanking God all the way that he hasn't gotten caught. Just before he slips back in the door, he turns to take one last look at the world he has known.

Luther stays up most of the night trying to get all of the ink off of his hand. Even with the ink remover, he has to scrub and scrub; but he finally gets it off. As he looks at his blood-red hand, he thinks about the many people he has been able to help by providing them with food and water. He also realizes that had it not been for the counterfeit mark, he probably would have been dead long ago.

Luther eventually falls into a deep sleep; and it isn't until late in the morning that a guard comes for him and says, "The captain wants to see you again." Luther follows the guard down the hall to Shaw's office where the captain says a pleasant good morning and then asks, "Luther, have you decided what you'd like to do?"

"Sir, I'm sorry, but I haven't yet decided."

"Now, Luther, there has to be a reason why you're hesitating. I'll give you a couple more days, but then that's it."

Luther manages to flash a fake smile and say, "Thank you for your patience with me, Sir." The guard takes Luther back to his room; and in a short while, they bring him a very good breakfast. He knows that the captain must really need him since he's being so nice. As he sits there eating, he wonders if it wouldn't have been better just to have gotten the inevitable ordeal over with. He knows it's coming sooner or later anyway.

Two days later, the captain sends for Luther again and says, "Well, Luther, this is it; you've had plenty of time to make up your mind. So what's it going to be?"

Luther knows he has to answer. "Sir, you've been so good to me, but I just can't do it."

Luther sees the captain starting to get aggravated as he asks, "And why not? There has to be a reason. I've made you a terrific offer, and any normal guy would be more than happy to jump at such an opportunity."

Luther knows the time has come for the truth. "To be honest with you, I just couldn't kill people like the Beast Regime does."

Immediately, the captain's expression and

spirit change; and he suspects something is up. "Do you really have the Mark of the Beast?" he asks.

"No, I don't. I'm a Christian, so I could never take the Mark; it would damn my soul forever."

All of a sudden, it's like an explosion has gone off; and all hell boils over. Blasphemies begin to pour out of the captain's mouth; and he jumps to his feet, nearly out of his mind with devil power. He grabs Luther and begins shoving him toward the door. Then he orders the guard to take him to the punishing cell and torture him without mercy. "How you ever got by the Beast Regime," he shouts, "I'll never know."

Just then, he jerks up Luther's right hand and sees how red it is where Luther has scrubbed the counterfeit mark off. He's furious as he glares at Luther and says, "I can't believe it! What did you put on that hand of yours?" Luther doesn't answer; and the captain yells, "Get this imbecile out of my sight! I can't believe I fell for his scheme! Take him to the punishing cell at once, and I'll be the one to decide how he'll die."

They lead Luther away, and three guards beat him almost to death. He's barely even semiconscious when they throw him on an old, bloodstained cot and shut the door. He doesn't know how many hours he lies there motionless, and he's in such a fog when he begins to come to that he can't even remember what happened to him.

Later, a guard shows up and says with great contempt, "Captain Shaw sent me to tell you that since you're such a good Christian, you'll be crucified at nine o'clock in the morning. He said he knew you'd appreciate dying just like your ridiculous Savior did about 2000 years ago. He also said to tell you that those two lunatic men who claim they've come down from Heaven with all power had better not show up. He's planning to have many extra, well-instructed Beast Regime soldiers there to get rid of those men once and for all, and the captain himself will be there to see it all well done."

Now that Luther's fully conscious, he can feel his body on fire all over; and he actually welcomes the message of death. Finally, he'll soon be in Heaven to see his wife and twins.

Luther's upcoming death creates a very big news story with the report even showing the crooked, upside-down cross he will die on—it resembles one used years ago that was a great sign of power. When they take Luther out to the prison yard the next morning, they beat him all the way. He had already suffered excruciating pain all night long, and now he's a bloody mess.

The news media has done their job well, and thousands show up to watch Luther's crucifixion. They nail him to the cross as the crowd jeers and mocks, but he's been beaten so badly that he can't make a sound. Tears stream down his cheeks because he's in so much pain; and then someone shouts, "Now you see how ridiculous you've been to have trusted in a man called Jesus who claimed to be the Son of God!"

Others join in and begin to taunt him further saying, "Jesus was an impostor and an arch deceiver!" Just then, it's as if Luther's vocal chords are suddenly set free; and he musters enough energy to begin singing:

At the Cross, at the Cross,
Where I first saw the light,
And the burden of my heart rolled away.
It was there by faith, I received my sight,
And now I am happy all the day.

It's truly God's miracle, and the crowd is immediately silenced. Then out of nowhere, the two witnesses appear proclaiming the eternal Gospel. One of them boldly declares, "We have come down from Heaven. Jesus is the true Son of Jehovah God and the only Savior; no other name will save you. The Bible plainly states that you who have the Mark are damned. There is no salvation for anyone who takes the Mark of the Beast."

Luther's face lights up with the glory of Jesus, and he gives the two witnesses a big smile of relief. "This is 'go home' day for me," Luther tells them. "I'll soon be in Heaven with my lovely wife and boys all because of Jesus. I know Jesus loves me and that He died for me so I could one day go to His Heaven."

While Luther hangs there dying, the crowd starts to throw things at him; and the Beast Regime moves in to stop the witnesses from preaching God's Holy Word. But just as they do, lightning flashes and the thunder roars. Then fire shoots out of the witnesses' mouths, and all of those soldiers who are supposed to have been so highly trained begin to fall over dead. The Earth literally reels and rocks underneath them, scaring the people to death as they run for their lives.

Soon, there's nothing but mass hysteria, and the soldiers want to run away, too; but they know they don't dare. However, as the fire continues to shoot out of the mouths of the witnesses and kill more and more of the soldiers, many of them take off anyway. The hundreds from the Beast Regime who had been there in the beginning are nearly all dead, and bodies are strewn everywhere.

Then Luther's words come forth loud and clear once again, "Victory in Jesus is mine! Thank God for Jesus!" Luther had been beaten almost to death before being cruci-fied, but God has given him the strength to shout one last message just before he dies. After the massacre is over, not a soldier is left, including Captain Shaw; and many other people with the Mark of the Beast have also been killed. The moment Luther dies, the witnesses disappear. They had come to help him win over the Beast and to preach the Gospel to all who were there.

The Bible prophesied that the witnesses would be on Earth for three-and-a-half years, and the two men are coming to the end of their mission. The Beast had set himself up in the temple of God and claimed to be the one and only true god, but the witnesses have stripped him of his claim; and people throughout the Earth are beginning to question him. They see that the witnesses have greater power than that of the Beast and all of the soldiers in his regime.

The Beast rages with anger at the news of the witnesses killing hundreds of his soldiers when Luther was crucified, and the news quickly spreads all over the world. He declares to all the captains of his regime that he's holding them personally responsible for what happened and that the two witnesses must be killed. In fact, he gives them an ultimatum—either the witnesses die, or all the captains will be put to death. The captains, now filled with stifling fear, are forced to go forth to try to kill the deadly and seemingly indestructible witnesses.

For several weeks, the captains try to fulfill their dangerous mission—to find the witnesses and kill them. Since the witnesses' work on Earth is now finished, God Almighty does allow the Regime to eventually find them and kill them. **And when they shall have finished their testimony, the beast that ascendeth out of the bottomless pit shall make war against them, and shall overcome them, and kill them** (Revelation 11:7). Only because God allows it are the witnesses able to be killed—it couldn't have happened any other way.

After this seemingly amazing victory, the Beast and all of his followers celebrate and dance in the streets; and for three-and-a-half days, the Beast won't allow the witnesses to be buried. He wants the whole world to see their dead bodies lying in the street and know that he and his regime have won.

And their dead bodies shall lie in the street of the great city, which spiritually is called Sodom and Egypt, where also our Lord was crucified. And they of the people and kindreds and tongues and nations shall see their dead bodies three days and an half, and shall not suffer their dead bodies to be put in graves. And they that dwell upon the earth shall rejoice over them, and make merry, and shall send gifts one to another; because these two prophets tormented them that dwelt on the earth (Revelation 11:8–10). People are so happy and excited that it's like Christmas, and they begin celebrating and giving gifts to one another. Their wretched tormentors are finally dead.

Then in the midst of the worldwide jubilation, a shocking event takes place that stuns the world. **After three days and an half the Spirit of life from God entered into them, and they** [the two witnesses] **stood upon their feet; and great fear fell upon them**

which saw them. And they heard a great voice from heaven saying unto them, Come up hither. And they ascended up to heaven in a cloud; and their enemies beheld them (Revelation 11:11,12).

The celebration is abruptly cut short when God resurrects the two witnesses right before the eyes of the whole world. He's proving to people that although anyone can take a life, only the true and living God can give life. His message to the Earth is, "I am God, and only I give life. I sent my witnesses from Heaven to Earth with my message, and they delivered it to you. I allowed them to be killed; but now I have given them life, and I'm bringing them home. Come on home, my Sons; you've finished your mission."

The God of Heaven clearly proves that He's mighty and has all power, and He doesn't stop with just resurrecting His two witnesses and taking them to Heaven. **And the same hour was there a great earthquake, and the tenth part of the city fell, and in the earthquake were slain of men seven thousand: and the remnant were affrighted, and gave glory**

336

to the God of heaven. The second woe is past, and, behold, the third woe cometh quickly. And the seventh angel sounded; and there were great voices in heaven, saying, The kingdoms of this world are become the kingdoms of our Lord, and of his Christ; and he shall reign forever and ever** (Revelation 11:13–15). People will have to realize once and for all that Jesus is the one and only door into Heaven; there is no other way to make it in.

CHAPTER
TWELVE

The days seem to fly by for Peter as the Tribulation Period continues. The false christ is keeping his promises—he has caused craft to prosper and people throughout the Earth have plenty of work. He's also dividing the money, the spoil, with people just as he said he would; and multitudes flock to support him.

The Jews in Israel and all over the world are jubilant because they think their Savior has come at last, but Peter knows the truth—they're headed for an awful shock in the middle of the seven-year covenant that their leaders have signed with the Beast. His people, the Jews, have already been through so much persecution, and his heart goes out to them; but through his knowledge of the book of Revelation, he finds comfort in knowing that they will have a chance to accept the real Christ as their true Messiah. Nevertheless, Peter knows that only one-third of the Jews will do that.

Peter realizes that time is getting short for the rest of the world, too—the first three-and-a-half years are almost up. The false peace will soon come to an end, and the true Christians will have to go underground to gather and worship their Lord God Almighty. Sorrow and despair have already started to cover the world, and many people are still searching for their missing loved ones; they're determined to never give up. The people who have found Jesus are the only ones with true peace.

Then just as Peter expects, the shocking news spreads all over the world: The Beast has broken his covenant with the Jews. They realize they have been deceived by the arch deceiver, and they run for their lives into the wilderness as the book of Revelation prophesied they would. Now, people will have to take the Mark of the world's dictator. He's definitely the devil-man.

Unbeknownst to most of those on Earth at this time, a great war is waging in Heaven. The archangel, Michael, and the good angels fight against the devil and his angels; and the devil is defeated. As a result, he and all of his devil angels are cast down to the Earth. **And there was war in heaven: Michael and his angels fought against the dragon; and the dragon fought and his angels, And prevailed not; neither was their place found any more in heaven. And the great dragon was cast out, that old serpent, called the Devil, and Satan, which deceiveth the whole world: he was cast out into the earth, and his angels were cast out with him. And I heard a loud voice saying in heaven, Now is come salvation, and strength, and the kingdom of our God, and the power of his Christ** (Revelation 12:7–10).

For thousands of years, the devil has been the prince of the air and able to fly at will up to one of the heavens to torment God by bringing accusations against His people. But after this heavenly war, he and his angels are cast down to the Earth at last to never again be able to fly through the air. **For the accuser of our brethren is cast down, which accused them before our God day and night. And they overcame him by the blood of the Lamb, and by the word of their testimony; and they loved not their lives unto the death. Therefore rejoice, ye heavens, and ye that dwell in them. Woe to the inhabiters of the earth and of the sea! for the devil is come down unto you, having great wrath, because he knoweth that he hath but a short time** (Revelation 12:10–12).

This overwhelming defeat sets the devil on an evil rampage more violent than ever before because he knows he has just a short time left to work. His mission is and always has been to do everything he possibly can to defeat those who serve God, but the Bible plainly declares that he will be the ultimate loser. God's people will overcome the devil.

They overcame him by the blood of the Lamb, and by the word of their testimony [or the Word that they put in their testimony] (Revelation 12:11).

Peter has carefully studied the end times in the Bible, so he knew all of this was coming. He's also well aware of what's in store for his people, the Jews. Revelation chapter twelve states, **And there appeared a great wonder in heaven; a woman** [Israel] **clothed with the sun, and the moon under her feet, and upon her head a crown of twelve stars: And she being with child cried, travailing in birth, and pained to be delivered. And there appeared another wonder in heaven; and behold a great red dragon, having seven heads and ten horns, and seven crowns upon his heads. And his tail drew the third part of the stars of heaven, and did cast them to the earth: and the dragon stood before the woman which was ready to be delivered, for to devour her child as soon as it was born. And she brought forth a man child, who was to rule all nations with a rod of iron: and her child was caught up unto**

God, and to his throne. And the woman fled into the wilderness, where she hath a place prepared of God, that they should feed her there a thousand two hundred and threescore days (Revelation 12:1–6). The man-child represents 144,000 of the Jews who take Jesus to be their Savior and then are caught up to God and to His throne.

Peter knows that John had said the man-child, the 144,000, would rule all nations with a rod of iron; but he wonders how that could be if they're in Heaven? He knows the Bible is the truth and that God doesn't lie; so he reasons with the Lord and comes to the conclusion that they will rule nations just as the Bible said but not until the Perfect Age, a 1000-year Millennium during which Christ will reign on Earth. Peter is already looking forward to that magnificent time of true peace, joy and happiness.

And I looked, and, lo, a Lamb stood on the mount Sion, and with him an hundred forty and four thousand, having his Father's name written in their foreheads... These were redeemed from among men,

being the firstfruits unto God and to the Lamb. And in their mouth was found no guile: for they are without fault before the throne of God (Revelation 14:1,4,5). The 144,000 redeemed Jews include 12,000 from each of the twelve tribes of Israel; and when they're actually caught up to Heaven, the world is shocked and bewildered that so many young Jewish men have just disappeared. The relatively few people who know the Bible and understand that the men are the first fruits of the Jewish harvest aren't alarmed, but the majority of the people once again don't know what to do.

The remaining Jews flee for their lives into the wilderness, overwhelmed with great sorrow and despair because they now realize that they had allowed themselves to be deceived by the Beast. Finally, many of them are coming into the knowledge that Jesus has been their true Messiah all along, and what a heartbreaking revelation that is. Those who accept Christ take consolation in knowing that God will take care of them, and those who do not will die.

When Peter hears the news of the 144,000 Jews being raptured, he knows great sorrow and tribulation will soon come. The Beast has already set himself up in the temple and shown himself to be Lord God Almighty. He has desecrated the holy temple of God, and Peter knows there will only be more deceit to come from the devil's kingdom.

Beginning immediately, no one can buy or sell without the Mark; and all it costs people to take it is their souls. Those who take the Mark become like the devil himself and never again will be able to get right with God or step foot in His Heaven. They have blasphemed against the Holy Ghost, and there is no forgiveness for that in this world or in the life to come. **Whosoever shall speak a word against the Son of man, it shall be forgiven him: but unto him that blasphemeth against the Holy Ghost it shall not be forgiven** (Luke 12:10). Peter is so thankful that the Lord gave him the wisdom of how to safeguard his money and prepare for this time.

When the two witnesses come down from

Heaven and begin preaching the everlasting Gospel, Peter knows they're real and that they've truly been sent by God. They're able to move at will because they have glorified bodies. They can go wherever they want to, whenever they want to.

He knows the witnesses will wage war against the Beast and his regime, but he's still in awe each time he sees the fire shoot out of their mouths and completely annihilate the soldiers of the Beast Regime. Who could have ever imagined such an unbelievable thing? The news is full of the death and destruction the witnesses are bringing about all over the world. The Regime soldiers are scared stiff and afraid to do their jobs. Even the Beast himself is afraid of them and has hidden himself away. They're killing the Beast's followers with God's fire and calling down plagues of destruction and torture in every nation. Millions are dying at the hands of the witnesses.

One time, Peter actually sees the two witnesses from Heaven appear dressed in sackcloth when a group of Beast Regime soldiers are beating up some children of God. One of the witnesses demands, "Let them go"; and one of the more arrogant soldiers immediately lashes out at the witness, but fire shoots out of his mouth and instantly kills the soldier.

Another one of the soldiers even haughtier than the first also tries to hit one of the witnesses, but fire again shoots out of the witness' mouth and kills him, too. With that, the rest of the soldiers come running, but fire explodes out of the mouths of the witnesses and kills about thirty of them. The people watching all of this are scared to death and frantically run for cover; but since Peter is a child of God, he knows he doesn't have to run. He's glad the witnesses have come.

Besides killing people with fire, the witnesses have the power to call down all kinds of plagues at will. **And I will give power unto my two witnesses, and they shall prophesy a thousand two hundred and threescore days, clothed in sackcloth. And if any man will hurt them, fire proceedeth out of their mouth, and devoureth their enemies: and if any man will hurt them, he must in this**

manner be killed. These have power to shut heaven, that it rain not in the days of their prophecy: and have power over waters to turn them to blood, and to smite the earth with all plagues, as often as they will (Revelation 11:3,5,6).

After a very short time, the period of grace for obtaining the Mark of the Beast ends; and the media immediately broadcasts that beginning the next day, the Beast Regime will start arresting those who refuse to take the Mark. All those who don't recant and take the Beast as their god will be tortured and put to death. Peter knows very well that this will endanger every Christian on Earth and that he and his Christian friends will no longer be able to meet at the church; they'll have to move their services underground. As quickly as possible, Peter warns everyone he can; then he sets up a secret meeting place where they can gather to worship God the Father and His Son, Jesus Christ.

Peter had already warned the people he knew to stock up on groceries and water and to be careful with their money because the

Bible plainly prophesied that food would be scarce and very expensive. He knows that hundreds of thousands of people will die because of this so-called savior.

As prophesied, the days pass by; and things get progressively worse. The Beast is determined that people will take his Mark or die a hideous death...and Christians are being killed every day. Peter's prayer for them is always, "Lord, help them to be strong." Through it all, one thought always haunts him: "If we hadn't been so foolish and had listened to the Word of God, we would all be in Heaven today. Oh, if only we had been ready for the one flight out."

Peter has been gathering information about the black market to see if it's going to be safe to use. He has been told that all those selling have the Mark, but he's also heard that they won't turn a Christian in. They don't care whom they sell to; they just want money, and Peter is thankful that he has plenty of it. He will most likely have enough for the duration of the Tribulation Period.

As he had planned all along, Peter is able to

help others by buying food and delivering it to those in need in the underground meetings. The people are always happy and grateful for his generosity; but Peter also warns them, "Don't tell a soul where you got this food. All of our lives are at stake, and you can't trust anyone. Also, please don't invite strangers to our meetings; we can't open them up to others like we used to."

Peter then instructs everyone, "You must get ready for the third appearance of Jesus Christ. He came the first time as the Lamb of God, and He still had that Lamb personality when He came the second time. However, the Bible plainly tells us in Revelation that when He comes the third time, He will come as the fierce Lion of the tribe of Judah; and every person on Earth will see Him. **Behold, he cometh with clouds; and every eye shall see him, and they also which pierced him: and all kindreds of the earth shall wail because of him** (Revelation 1:7)." Peter can't wait to see his Lord suspended in the air above the Earth and ready to do battle against the powers of the devil.

One thing that saddens Peter's heart is thinking of the great sorrow and grief the Jews will go through when they realize what they have done to their Messiah. **And they shall look upon me whom they have pierced, and they shall mourn for him, as one mourneth for his only son, and shall be in bitterness for him, as one that is in bitterness for his firstborn** (Zechariah 12:10).

In spite of that revelation, two-thirds of the Jewish people are not going to change. They'll remain arrogant and rebellious, and they'll die because of refusing to accept the true Messiah, Jesus Christ. **And it shall come to pass, that in all the land, saith the LORD, two parts therein shall be cut off and die; but the third shall be left therein. And I will bring the third part through the fire, and will refine them as silver is refined, and will try them as gold is tried: they shall call on my name, and I will hear them: I will say, It is my people: and they shall say, The LORD is my God** (Zechariah 13:8,9).

As the days wear on, Peter studies the Word

more and more. He knows the Bible has laid out all that will take place, and he wants to know exactly what's going to happen next. Revelation was where he learned all about the coming of the Beast and what he would bring on the Earth. First, it said he would bring false peace to draw people in and that he would use that peace to destroy them. **And I saw, and behold a white horse: and he that sat on him had a bow; and a crown was given unto him: and he went forth conquering, and to conquer. And there went out another horse that was red: and power was given to him that sat thereon to take peace from the earth, and that they should kill one another: and there was given unto him a great sword** (Revelation 6:2,4).

After the false peace is destroyed, the Word says the Beast would bring a great famine to the whole Earth which Peter and the rest of the world are now in the midst of. **And I beheld, and lo a black horse; and he that sat on him had a pair of balances in his hand. And I heard a voice in the midst of the four beasts say, A measure of wheat for**

a penny, and three measures of barley for a penny; and see thou hurt not the oil and the wine (Revelation 6:5,6). When this actually begins to take place, even bread becomes very scarce; and the price of it skyrockets so high that only the rich can afford it. Just one loaf of bread costs close to $150, and a mere bushel of wheat runs close to $3300.

Peter never ceases to thank the Lord that he and his parents were so blessed because he now has the money to buy what he needs and freely share with those who are depending on him. Peter is the kind of person who always thinks of others.

The Beast is no longer the great superman people thought he was, and he's being uncovered as the false christ he really is. People are no longer prospering, and death is everywhere. Daniel's little horn who had succeeded in deceiving people into thinking he was such a great savior is now bringing famine and death to the world. **And I looked, and behold a pale horse: and his name that sat on him was Death, and Hell followed with him. And power was given unto them**

over the fourth part of the earth, to kill with sword, and with hunger, and with death, and with the beasts of the earth (Revelation 6:8). Death is riding freely and beginning to consume the Earth; and now, nearly all of the news reports are about death, death, death. Peter never ceases to be amazed at how plainly God has laid out all that is happening.

Things take a sudden and dramatic change when the demonic locust beasts emerge from the bottomless pit and cover the Earth. Peter knew they would come, but he wasn't prepared for just how hideous and tormenting they really are. Even though he's a child of God, these beasts are still enough to frighten anyone to the core; and people can no longer die. **And unto them was given power, as the scorpions of the earth have power. And it was commanded them that they should not hurt the grass of the earth, neither any green thing, neither any tree; but only those men which have not the seal of God in their foreheads. And to them it was given that they should not kill them, but**

that they should be tormented five months: and their torment was as the torment of a scorpion, when he striketh a man (Revelation 9:3–5).

For five months, the repulsive locusts terrorize the Earth and torture those with the Mark of the Beast far beyond their worst nightmares. They suffer indescribable agony from which there is no relief. **And in those days shall men seek death, and shall not find it; and shall desire to die, and death shall flee from them** (Revelation 9:6).

One day, Peter finds himself face-to-face with one of the hideous beasts, and he feels as if he'll die of sheer terror right there on the spot; but he's relieved when it turns the other way. That beast was definitely the most repulsive thing Peter had ever seen. **And the shapes of the locusts were like unto horses prepared unto battle; and on their heads were as it were crowns like gold, and their faces were as the faces of men. And they had hair as the hair of women, and their teeth were as the teeth of lions. And they had breastplates, as it were breastplates of** iron; and the sound of their wings was as the sound of chariots of many horses running to battle. And they had tails like unto scorpions, and there were stings in their tails: and their power was to hurt men five months (Revelation 9:7–10). Thankfully, the beast didn't touch Peter because he had the seal of God on him.

After the locusts comes another nightmare—the huge army of deadly horsemen. People can once again die, but being tortured and killed by creatures that seem to come from hell itself is enough to send people out of their minds from sheer terror. **And the four angels were loosed, which were prepared for an hour, and a day, and a month, and a year, for to slay the third part of men. And the number of the army of the horsemen were two hundred thousand thousand: and I heard the number of them** (Revelation 9:15,16). This demonic army has 200 million horsemen, and their only assignment is to kill.

And thus I saw the horses in the vision, and them that sat on them, having breastplates

of fire, and of jacinth, and brimstone: and the heads of the horses were as the heads of lions; and out of their mouths issued fire and smoke and brimstone. By these three was the third part of men killed, by the fire, and by the smoke, and by the brimstone, which issued out of their mouths. For their power is in their mouth, and in their tails: for their tails were like unto serpents, and had heads, and with them they do hurt** (Revelation 9:17–19). Being attacked by one of these hellish creatures is far worse than anything seen in even the most extreme horror film ever created.

Amidst all of this unimaginable terror, there are angels from Heaven flying above and preaching the Gospel of Christ. **And I saw another angel fly in the midst of heaven, having the everlasting gospel to preach unto them that dwell on the earth, and to every nation, and kindred, and tongue, and people** (Revelation 14:6). Peter can't forget the first time he saw one of those preaching angels in the sky, and it amazed him to know that the message could be heard all over the world and be understood by all people no matter what language they spoke.

Every time Peter hears the glorious Gospel go forth from heavenly beings, it thrills his soul through and through. Over and over, Peter encourages the people in his services to study the book of Revelation stressing, "It tells you that God is not only using His angels to pour out judgments upon the Earth but also to preach the Gospel of Christ to the whole world. Hallelujah, Children! The Beast and all of his followers have to listen to their message even though they despise it. They can't get away from the truth, and they hate it; but those of us who love the truth should be encouraged and so thankful that we have refused to take the Mark of doom. Praise God!"

The world is full of so much death, destruction and torment; but the angels' message temporarily lifts the minds of Christians above all of that. In addition to the angels of the Gospel, there are other angels sounding heavenly trumpets that shake the whole Earth; and Peter can actually feel the ground moving back and forth under his feet.

Peter keeps himself very busy. He and the underground Christians continue to have great services, and he becomes more and more involved in the underground black market. People have discovered that he's very wealthy, so those who are selling want his money whether he has the Mark or not. Peter has never figured out how so much food is made available underground, but he really doesn't care as long as he can get what he needs.

Surprisingly, J.C. Blem now stays with Peter most of the time. J.C. was forced to give up his newspaper job in the middle of the Tribulation Period, and all of the other workers were also forced to leave; but Peter's happy that most of them began attending the services at his church and are now saved. Since J.C., his wife, his daughter and her husband had received salvation, they had fallen in love with Peter and become great blessings to him. They always help him in the services and in the distribution of food and water.

When J.C. was put out of the newspaper

business, Peter no longer had a job; but he didn't give up the business entirely. He wants all of the Beast's followers to see his God in action, so he often carries a small video camera in his coat pocket; and whenever he sees the two witnesses killing people or the devastating results of their plagues, he secretly shoots it. He even captures people being attacked by the demonic locust beasts and the devilish horsemen creatures. Yes, it's terrifying and sickening to watch, but Peter is determined that people see the power of the true God.

When Peter gets some footage that he thinks is really good, he sells it to a contact in the underground market. That person then resells it for even more money to the news stations. Peter's contact never turns him in because he wants the money, and the stations pay his contact very well.

The news stations never make a big deal over it because they can't get that kind of footage any other way. All of the stations' cameramen and reporters have the Mark or they wouldn't have been able to keep their jobs. Therefore, every time one of the witnesses, locust creatures or horsemen beasts shows up, the reporters and cameramen run away as fast as they can so they won't be killed or stung. Peter, however, is a child of God; so although he's scared, he knows the witnesses and the beasts won't touch him.

Now, that doesn't mean Peter isn't in great danger because he is. If the Beast or the Regime ever find out what he's doing, Peter knows he'll surely be killed. Nevertheless, he thinks the great risk is worth it for the honor and glory of his Lord. Peter has had some narrow escapes from the Beast Regime; but somehow, the Lord has always delivered him.

Regardless of what's going on, Peter spends most of his time in prayer and in helping others find Jesus. He does his best to make sure people are as strong in the Lord as they possibly can be so that if they're arrested, they won't take the Mark no matter how severely they're tortured. People can't afford to sell their souls to the devil because if they stand true to the Lord Jesus, they'll soon be with Him forever.

Peter has been fortunate enough to remain in his home, so he can always keep up with the latest news and is a great help to all of the Christians who are forced underground. He still loves stories about the two witnesses and is always fascinated by how the power of God is used through them. He can never get enough of watching them move like the angels, call down plagues and kill entire armies of the Beast's followers at one time. He knows they're truly God's men, and he finds it so satisfying to see the supposedly all-powerful Beast Regime soldiers scared out of their wits and running for their lives. To the witnesses, they're just devilish nobodies they can kill in a split second or torture beyond words with any number of plagues.

As time goes on, more and more of the prophecies of Revelation become reality; and in addition to what the world has already endured, angels begin pouring out the seven vials of the wrath of God upon the Earth. **And I heard a great voice out of the temple saying to the seven angels, Go your ways, and pour out the vials of the wrath of God** upon the earth (Revelation 16:1).

And the first [angel] **went, and poured out his vial upon the earth; and there fell a noisome and grievous sore upon the men which had the mark of the beast, and upon them which worshipped his image** (Revelation 16:2). God's wrath is not yet finished with the arrogant followers of the devil. **Thy pomp is brought down to the grave, and the noise of thy viols: the worm is spread under thee, and the worms cover thee** (Isaiah 14:11). God covers the people's bodies with grotesque sores which cause excruciating pain inside and out. When God pours out His wrath, nothing can stop it; and nothing can stand before it. God warned people in His Bible what they would suffer if they sold their souls to the devil.

After this first vial judgment, Peter declares out loud and warns the other Christians, "God is using angels to send His wretched judgments of wrath upon all who have the Mark of the Beast."

And the second angel poured out his vial upon the sea; and it became as the blood

of a dead man: and every living soul died in the sea [including people on boats and ships] (Revelation 16:3). Peter is appalled to actually see that every creature in the sea has died as well as all people who were in or on the sea at the time. The foul, sickening stench of death nauseates people for miles. News commentators show up on TV wearing face masks because the overwhelming and suffocating odor of rotting flesh is enough to kill anyone.

And the third angel poured out his vial upon the rivers and fountains of waters; and they became blood. And I heard the angel of the waters say, Thou art righteous, O Lord, which art, and wast, and shalt be, because thou hast judged thus. For they have shed the blood of saints and prophets, and thou hast given them blood to drink; for they are worthy (Revelation 16:4–6). The Beast Regime and those who honor the Beast have shed so much blood that the Lord feels they should have blood to drink. Because of this judgment, people in some sections of the world have no drinking water at all;

and many thousands have already died and are still dying of thirst. People shouldn't be surprised because God said, **Vengeance is mine; I will repay** (Romans 12:19).

And I heard another out of the altar say, Even so, Lord God Almighty, true and righteous are thy judgments (Revelation 16:7). The angels of God themselves bear witness that the Lord is using them to pour out the deadly vials of judgment, but they also declare that God is just in doing so. People who reject God deserve all the punishment He pours out on them, especially after the way they have sold their souls to the devil and taken the Mark of the Beast.

And the fourth angel poured out his vial upon the sun; and power was given unto him to scorch men with fire (Revelation 16:8). The Bible also declares in Isaiah that God will burn many men to death. **Therefore hath the curse devoured the earth, and they that dwell therein are desolate: therefore the inhabitants of the earth are burned, and few men left** (Isaiah 24:6). Peter watches literally thousands die as the fourth vial is being poured out. The judgments of God have become so cruel and destructive that Peter can hardly take it all in.

And men were scorched with great heat, and blasphemed the name of God, which hath power over these plagues: and they repented not to give him glory (Revelation 16:9). Thousands of people with the Mark are being burned to death while many others are being scorched with heat and left with severe burns all over their bodies, but these devil-possessed people still curse the God of Heaven and refuse to repent. They still blame God for their situation instead of themselves, and they hate and despise Him for making them suffer the pains of hell.

And the fifth angel poured out his vial upon the seat of the beast; and his kingdom was full of darkness; and they gnawed their tongues for pain (Revelation 16:10). This darkness is so total and complete without a hint of light anywhere that it totally envelopes people, and it's almost suffocating. They can actually feel it, and it causes those who have the Mark to gnaw their tongues in pain. God even pours out darkness on the seat of the Beast, and the false christ has no power to overcome it. His subjects are seeing that although he has set himself up in the temple of God and showed himself to be God, he doesn't have any power over Lord God Almighty.

The devil himself never has had and never will have any power over God, and He will soon cast Satan down into the pits of hell. When that happens, those who want to will be able to see the devil when he's in the bottomless pit; and they'll mock him saying, **Art thou also become weak as we? art thou become like unto us? How art thou fallen from heaven, O Lucifer, son of the morning! how art thou cut down to the ground, which didst weaken the nations! For thou hast said in thine heart, I will ascend into heaven, I will exalt my throne above the stars of God: I will sit also upon the mount of the congregation, in the sides of the north: I will ascend above the heights of the clouds; I will be like the most High. Yet thou shalt be brought down to**

hell, to the sides of the pit. They that see thee shall narrowly look upon thee, and consider thee, saying, Is this the man that made the earth to tremble, that did shake kingdoms; That made the world as a wilderness, and destroyed the cities thereof; that opened not the house of his prisoners (Isaiah 14:10,12–17)? The devil is nothing but a liar and a fake! Before the true and living God, he's weak and helpless.

And the sixth angel poured out his vial upon the great river Euphrates; and the water thereof was dried up, that the way of the kings of the east might be prepared (Revelation 16:12). When the bed of the great Euphrates River dries up, most people are totally shocked and bewildered as to how or why such a thing could happen. Most have never studied the Bible; so they don't know that the Lord is making a dry-land highway for the kings of the East, those from China and Japan, to use as a passage to Jerusalem for the Battle of Armageddon.

Peter knows the truth; and when he hears that the river has dried up completely, his heart leaps for joy because he knows it won't be much longer before Jesus will arrive to end the Tribulation Period. Then the Antichrist and Antispirit will finally be cast into the lake of fire.

And the seventh angel poured out his vial into the air; and there came a great voice out of the temple of heaven, from the throne, saying, It is done. And there were voices, and thunders, and lightnings; and there was a great earthquake, such as was not since men were upon the earth, so mighty an earthquake, and so great. And the great city [of Jerusalem] **was divided into three parts** [and a great valley runs between]**, and the cities of the nations fell: and great Babylon came in remembrance before God, to give unto her the cup of the wine of the fierceness of his wrath** (Revelation 16:17–19). Of all of the devastating earthquakes that have rocked the world, this one is by far the worst. It's so powerful that it completely destroys every big city throughout the world—Los Angeles, Chicago, New York, Tokyo, London, Moscow, and the list goes on and on. The Earth is fighting the biggest battle of its existence and losing miserably as it rings with the screams of those feeling the pains of hell without any hope. Millions of people lose their lives because of the fierceness of God's wrath.

One of the most astonishing things about this massive earthquake is that it doesn't destroy Jerusalem. Instead, it divides the city into three parts and creates an enormous valley in between them. Peter knows that God is further preparing that area for the soon-coming Battle of Armageddon. "Oh," he thinks to himself, "if only people could know what they're headed for."

As if the devastating, worldwide earthquake isn't enough, gigantic hailstones like the world has never seen before begin raining down from the sky with supernatural force. **And every island fled away, and the mountains were not found. And there fell upon men a great hail out of heaven, every stone about the weight of a talent** [almost 100 lbs]**: and men blasphemed God because of the plague of the hail; for the plague**

thereof was exceeding great (Revelation 16:20,21). Peter stands spellbound as he watches the news reports of huge hailstones weighing about 100 pounds each just pouring out of the sky and destroying everyone and everything in their path. God's great fury is being unleashed on all of the ungodliness on Earth with a fierceness Peter never imagined; but even then, men don't repent but instead blaspheme God for the deadly plague.

They had all been warned, **It is a fearful thing to fall into the hands of the living God** (Hebrews 10:31); but people paid no attention.

CHAPTER
THIRTEEN

After the Rapture took place, three young girls—Patsy Gardner, Suzanna Hilton and Delmar Johns—finally got saved at the church Peter attended. Since then, they have grown to really love each other and their Lord; and they have become members of Peter's underground church. They're grateful for the anointed services and that the Lord has made a way for them to continue gathering to worship, but the church where they got saved is very special to them. It completely changed their lives, so they decide to go back there one last time. They know they have to be careful not to let any Beast Regime soldiers see them, so they wind their way there through many back roads and slip in the back door.

Once inside, they're completely over-whelmed with God's presence and very grateful and thankful to kneel again at that blessed altar. They get so carried away in praising the Lord that they forget to keep an eye out for the soldiers; and suddenly, they hear heavy footsteps in the aisles. Their blood runs cold as they quickly turn to see soldiers of the Beast Regime racing toward them; and within minutes, all three of them are arrested and on their way to prison.

When they arrive, they're forced into one of the backyard areas by the snake pit. A stocky, devilish-looking soldier almost seems to hiss as he says, "Now, Girls, take a good look into that pit because all three of you will become the next victims of these beautiful, poisonous creatures."

Just then, two men raise the lid from a large, deep pit. When the three girls peer down into it and see that it's filled with hundreds of huge, slimy, slithering snakes, their eyes fly wide open; and they're overcome with paralyzing fear. Their hearts are racing so fast that they can hardly catch their breath as they realize what their fate is going to be; but even so, they know they'll never take the Mark of the Beast. They're also well aware that neither Peter nor anyone else can help them; so right away, they begin to pray that God will make them strong.

The three girls sleep very little that night; and early the next morning, two disgusting guards come for them. They take them back out to the snake pit; and when they choose Patsy to die first, the other girls become hysterical. As usual, many people with the Mark have gathered to watch them die; and the foulmouthed guard snarls, "Patsy, will you take the Mark?"

"No! I will never take that Mark of doom!" she boldly declares. "The Lord is my Savior; Jesus Christ is the true Son of God, and I will soon be in Heaven with Him! Jesus is King of kings and Lord of lords!" The guards can't stand the sound of her voice, so they quickly throw her into the snake pit. Suzanna and Delmar are forced to watch as the slimy snakes cover her body, biting her until she stops moving and takes her last breath.

Suzanna feels like she's going to vomit as the guards turn to her. She can hardly move; but she manages to give Delmar a big hug and whisper, "I'll meet you in Heaven." Delmar doesn't know how she can possibly watch another one of her dear friends die an agonizing death, so she prays as hard as she can that God will make her strong through His divine blood. She closes her eyes as the guard asks Suzanna if she'll recant and take the Mark; and Suzanna immediately cries with a loud voice, "I'll never take the Mark! Jesus is the Son of God, the only true Almighty God in Heaven. The Beast is a fake!" The guards quickly shove her into the pit and force Delmar to open her eyes. Again, she has to watch what looks like hundreds of demonic-looking snakes slither over her friend, striking and biting every inch of her body; and she has to hear her shrieks of pain. Not until Suzanna takes her last breath do they turn to Delmar.

By this time, Delmar is shaking so violently that she can hardly stand or see straight; and she just wants to go to Heaven. So when the guard turns to ask her if she will take the Mark, she doesn't even let him finish before she shouts, "Jesus victory is mine! Oh, Jesus, you died for me; and I'm coming home!" The crowd starts chanting blasphemies and cursing as the guards pick her up and throw her in as hard as they can. She hits the bottom with a thud; and immediately, a large boa constrictor curls around her body and squeezes the life out of her. She doesn't even feel the other snakes biting her because she's already with the Lord.

Peter happens to turn on the news just as the girls are being led to the pit, and he is almost beside himself because he didn't even know they had been arrested. He immediately cries out, "Oh, God, these girls have been such a big help to me and have brought so many lost souls to be saved. Please help them!" After forcing himself to watch all three girls die a victorious death, he is finally able to shout, "Hallelujah! They have won."

In the latter part of the Tribulation Period, the Beast Regime steps up their efforts to find and execute those without the Mark, and J.C. Blem's daughter and son-in-law are next on the list. Buck and Laney Holiday had gotten saved after their little, four-year-old boy was taken with Jesus on the one flight out, but they could never get over Jimmy being gone. Nevertheless, the Lord had continued to help them; they had become real soul winners and were a big help to Peter and his work for the Lord. They had helped him deliver many loads of groceries to people who had gotten saved and were determined never to take the Mark of the Beast.

Buck and Laney had gotten up early one morning to take some desperately needed food to a shut-in couple who had not taken the Mark; however, soldiers of the Beast were watching the couple's house, and Buck and Laney were arrested as soon as they arrived. When they didn't return after making the delivery, Peter just knew they had to have fallen into the hands of the Regime.

When J.C. hears that Buck and Laney have

been arrested, he and his wife can hardly contain their grief; and they call Peter at once for prayer. J.C. desperately wants God to help his daughter and her husband to be able to stand strong through the divine blood of Jesus. He also wants prayer for his wife, Verdie, because she's taking it all so hard.

Peter's heart goes out to them; but as much as he wants to help them, he knows the only thing they can do is pray that God will help them to stand firm and refuse the Mark...and he feels sure they will because he knows how much they love the Lord. He also knows that they'll never give up the hope of seeing their little Jimmy again; they talked about him all the time. They knew it was impossible for them to have another child since the Lord had now made every woman sterile and would not allow one baby to be born during the Tribulation Period; and even if they could have conceived, they wouldn't have wanted to bring a child into such a horrible world.

J.C. and Verdie know it will be impossible for them to see Buck and Laney in prison, so they just nervously sit and wait until they hear news of their scheduled deaths. Peter's the one who finally hears the date and that they will be fed to vicious lions that have been brought in specifically for the purpose of killing people. The Regime feeds the lions nothing but human bodies.

Peter doesn't know whether or not their deaths will be shown on TV because so many people have been killed recently for refusing to take the Mark that the city's Regime captain thinks it makes him look like a failure for not being able to convince more people to recant. Peter doesn't think he can stomach watching any more deaths anyway; but if their deaths are broadcast, he knows he'll have to watch and hold them up in prayer as they stand for Christ.

The morning that Buck and Laney are to die, the Beast Regime makes a bigger deal out of it than usual because they feel that too many people are holding out on them and not taking the Mark; so the captain himself brings them out together. Buck and Laney follow along arm-in-arm, seemingly fearless. They move as if they're in a glorious trance, not even noticing what's going on around them. They don't seem to hear the crowd sneering and mocking, "We know where our god is; where is yours?"

The captain tries his best to talk them into taking the Mark. "I can tell you two really love each other and that you want nothing more than to spend the rest of your lives together, so why don't you take the Mark and continue your journey with each other? Wouldn't that be the best thing for you and your family?"

After a few minutes of silence, Buck seems to come to himself; and he responds with the great love of Jesus Christ. "I can answer for both of us when I say that we will never take the Mark. It's the Mark of blasphemy, and it would damn us forever before the only true God who made Heaven and Earth. Our little boy, Jimmy, was on the one flight out, and we can't wait to get to Heaven to be with him."

The devil-possessed crowd goes stark-raving mad. They throw dirt in the air and shout all kinds of vulgar things, but Buck and Laney don't even seem to notice or pay attention.

The guards had thought the couple would put up a big fight when it came time to push them into the lions' den with such hungry, vicious beasts; but Buck and Laney calmly walk into the den on their own, praising God out loud for His saving grace through His Son, Jesus Christ, the real Savior of the world.

Their deaths were glorious! They had won over the Beast and the devil himself, and Peter's on his knees in front of the TV thanking the Lord for what he has just witnessed. He has never yet seen such victorious deaths. They were so calm, and their faces looked almost angelic; and he's grateful that the report didn't actually show their bodies being devoured. Little did he know that it was all part of God's plan.

The Regime captain had specifically arranged for the people watching on television to be able to hear and see the lions killing Buck and Laney and eating their bodies, but it didn't turn out as he had planned. As soon as the couple had walked into the den, lightning began to flash and thunder roared. Then the sun's light went completely out, and there was total darkness.

The crowd was suddenly silent, and at first they couldn't move; but the place soon erupted into mass hysteria, and many people were severely injured in a stampede. It was so dark that the cameras couldn't record a thing, but their microphones still picked up the frantic screams of the crowd loud and clear.

Peter and the other dedicated Christians had learned by now that no matter what happens, they have to carry on. So many people still need to be saved and helped that there's no time to give up, and Peter prays for more of God's strength every day.

Peter continues helping people find Jesus, and he still feeds as many of those without the Mark as he can. Yes, many of the Christians are being put to death in hideous, inhumane ways, but Peter works hard to get the people ready to die; and in doing so, it just makes him stronger. Peter lives to help others.

Although Peter's Jewish, he loves the Lord with all of his heart; and God has supplied him with millions of dollars so he can help people and get those saved who probably would have starved or taken the Mark. The Regime plays on those who are starving by trying to coax them to take the Mark with offers of food and water; but thanks to Peter, many people aren't as hungry and thirsty as the soldiers think they are. Everyone who knows Peter loves him, so none of those he helps ever breathe a word about what he does. His secret has remained safe.

The black-market business people had the Mark, but no one would have known that in their business dealings unless they saw it on them. They would take money from anyone because they loved it and just wanted as much of it as they could get—and Peter had plenty. In fact, they depended so much on Peter's money that they would have killed anybody who gave him away.

After the deaths of Laney and Buck and the three younger girls, the rest of the Christians in Peter's church work harder than ever to make up for the loss of such good workers. J.C. and Verdie have long since used up their money, but they're thankful to have been able to use it to help others. They didn't want the Beast to get a penny of it; however, he had managed to get control of a lot of other people's money, and he had shared the spoil with the people just like he had said he would.

Thankfully, Peter still has millions of dollars left; and he knows everything will be fine as long as he remains in charge of it, and the Beast Regime never finds it. He knows very well that the Lord is the one who has given him the knowledge and wisdom of exactly how to safeguard his money and use it, and he's thankful for it every day.

Everything seems to be going along as well as can be expected when calamity strikes again. Peter's good friends J.C. and Verdie are arrested by the Beast Regime, and it hits Peter like a ton of bricks. They have become like close family to him and have shown him so much love.

After the Blems are arrested, the Beast Regime discovers that J.C. had been the editor of the biggest newspaper in the city; so they really make a big deal out of his arrest. The Regime plots and plans his death and decides to burn J.C. and his wife at the stake so the whole city can enjoy their bonfire. Such devilish thoughts can only come from the pits of hell.

The guards put J.C. and Verdie together in the same cell, thinking that Verdie might possibly persuade her husband to take the Mark. The captain of the city's Beast Regime and some of the soldiers had known J.C. in the past, and they know he's a good leader with a strong personality; so they also decide to try to appeal to that.

After keeping the Blems in their cell for a few days, the captain decides to have a talk with them. "Mr. Blem," he begins, "you have a lot of valuable experience and so much going for you. Surely, you don't want to waste it all on a foolish God. It would be such a shame to have to burn someone with your experience at the stake. Wouldn't you prefer to go back to the big newspaper you loved so much? You always did such a great job, and then you and your wife could have a happy home once again."

Thankfully, J.C. loves his God more than

any worldly fame or fortune; and he immediately answers, "Nothing could convince
me to give up the Lord I serve and damn
my soul for all eternity. My wife and I serve
Jesus Christ, the true Son of God, who has
given us beautiful salvation and the air we
breathe. Even right now, we know He has
His loving arms around us; and we'll never
give Him up."

The captain starts to get angry as he says,
"You mean you don't care about your wife
any more than that? You actually want her
to be burned at the stake with you tomorrow
morning? So many people in this city know
who you are, and I know many of them will
show up here to enjoy your fabulous fire.
Surely, you don't want that to happen, do
you?" J.C. and Verdie don't budge; and in a
rage, the captain sends them away.

It's late by the time J.C. and Verdie return to
their cell; so they pray and then fall asleep in
each other's arms, knowing it will be their last
night on Earth. When they wake up early the
next morning, the first thing J.C. says to Verdie is, "Today we get to go home to Heaven

and see our lovely daughter and son-in-law and our darling little Jimmy. They both died such glorious deaths; and I pray that we'll be able to do the same."

Just as the captain had said, thousands have gathered in the prison yard and are anxiously waiting to see the couple be burned at the stake. As they're being led to the courtyard, Verdie whispers to J.C., "We're going to be all right, Honey; the Lord is with us." J.C. squeezes her hand and nods, "Yes, He is."

Because there are so many people, the guards want to put on a big show; so they really rough up the precious couple as they chain them to the stake, beating and taunting them the entire time. Then they take their time piling up the wood just right and pouring kerosene all around them and even over their heads. One last time, they're asked, "Will you recant and take the Mark of the Beast?" J.C. speaks right up without blinking an eye and answers, "No, we will not! Jesus is the only true Christ, the Son of the Almighty God who sits on His throne in Heaven."

The captain of the Beast Regime spits out

a stream of blasphemies against God and then cries, "Light the fire! They have lost their minds!"

The people in the crowd begin waving their arms in the air and shouting, "Honor to the Beast! Honor to the Beast!" as the flames rise higher and higher. It seems strange that neither J.C. nor Verdie have made even a whimper, so the people are a little disappointed that they died instantly; but then to their astonishment, they see a charred, black hand and arm rise up toward the sky and hear Verdie cry, "Jesus is King!" Then with her last breath, she cries out again, "I see Jesus sitting at the right hand of the Father. Lord God Almighty, we're coming home!"

The people immediately start throwing things into the fire and shouting such disgusting vulgarities that it has to be the language of hell. Then suddenly, the people feel the Earth begin reeling to and fro like a drunkard; and they hear loud voices proclaiming, "Jesus will soon come from Heaven as King of kings and Lord of lords." Then just like lightning, the two witnesses appear; and everyone can see that they're the ones shouting the Gospel message. The soldiers and the captain run for their lives without even trying to protect the people; but the witnesses quickly call down hailstones from Heaven upon them and kill them all, along with many in the crowd who have the Mark. Others die from being trampled to death as people desperately try to get away.

One haughty person hits one of the witnesses, but fire shoots out of his mouth and instantly kills that arrogant fool. Several other people try to shoot the witnesses; but instead, the fire-breathing men kill every one of them.

Peter prays hard for his two dear loved ones as he watches their morbid deaths on television, and he's so proud of God for the way they died. Peter tries to stop his tears by praising God that they're safely home, but he loved them so much that he's overwhelmed with grief. He knows that from here on out, he'll have to be more careful than ever because someone could easily report him to the Beast Regime.

Peter is still completely fascinated by the

two witnesses, and he doesn't like to think about the fact that their time on Earth is almost over; but he knows very well that the Bible says their mission will only last for three-and-a-half years.

When the time comes that God actually allows the Beast to wage war against the two witnesses, it's a worldwide event; and nearly every eye on Earth is glued to the TV for the entire battle. Peter doesn't want to see them die, but he knows it will happen. **And when they shall have finished their testimony, the beast that ascendeth out of the bottomless pit shall make war against them, and shall overcome them, and kill them** (Revelation 11:7).

Peter knows that the bodies of the witnesses will lie in the street for three-and-a-half days for the whole world to see. There used to be a time when Christians wondered how that could happen; but they now know that television, satellite and the Internet have made news and information available to all at any time...and God knew that would be the case. **And their dead bodies shall lie in the street** of the great city, which spiritually is called Sodom and Egypt, where also our Lord was crucified. And they of the people and kindreds and tongues and nations shall see their dead bodies three days and an half, and shall not suffer their dead bodies to be put in graves. And they that dwell upon the earth shall rejoice over them, and make merry, and shall send gifts one to another; because these two prophets tormented them that dwelt on the earth (Revelation 11:8–10).

After the witnesses are killed, Peter sees the Beast and those who have the Mark rejoicing and dancing in the streets and sending gifts to each other. It's just like Christmastime had been before the Tribulation Period began which shows that the devil is merely a copycat who tries to imitate the things of God for his own honor and glory.

The Beast and his followers are so happy to finally be free of the death and destruction of the witnesses, but it only lasts for three-and-a-half days. **And after three days and an half the Spirit of life from God entered**

**into them, and they stood upon their feet;
and great fear fell upon them which saw
them. And they heard a great voice from
heaven saying unto them, Come up hither.
And they ascended up to heaven in a cloud;
and their enemies beheld them** (Revelation
11:11,12). God is making sure that the world's
attention is focused on the witnesses before
He brings them to life and shows His great
power to all.

Peter waits anxiously by his TV because he
doesn't want to miss the resurrection of the
witnesses or their ascension back to Heaven.
He wants to see how people will react. Finally,
the big day comes; and when the witnesses
suddenly come back to life and stand up, the
demonic dancing comes to an abrupt halt,
and the people are paralyzed with unbelievable fear.

Peter stares in holy awe at what God is
doing, and then he laughs with great joy
when he sees all of the people running for
cover. They know all too well what the two
witnesses are capable of and how easily
they can kill hundreds or even thousands of

people at a time. They expect fire to shoot out of the prophets' mouths at any moment; but instead, they're shocked to hear a voice from Heaven saying, "Come up higher." The crowd stops dead in their tracks and watches as the two men ascend straight up to Glory. To most people, it's a frightening sight; but Peter thinks it's absolutely glorious!

Once Peter stops rejoicing and praising the Lord for such a beautiful manifestation, he immediately gets quiet...he knows that the great Battle of Armageddon is about to begin. He doesn't know whether to be happy or terrified, but there is one thing he knows without a doubt—he will soon see his Lord and Master, Jesus Christ, suspended in midair and ready to wage war against the Beast and all of his followers.

Peter has studied the battle many times, and he's ready to watch it unfold like a fabulous but terrifying action-packed movie for which he already knows the script. Without a doubt, it will be the fieriest and most devastating war ever to take place in the history of mankind.

CHAPTER
FOURTEEN

As prophesied, the nations begin gathering for the great Battle of Armageddon, and Peter's prepared to watch it all play out. **And the word of the LORD came unto me, saying, Son of man, set thy face against Gog** [Russia's leader]**, the land of Magog** [Russia]**, the chief prince of Meshech and Tubal, and prophesy against him, And say, Thus saith the Lord GOD; Behold, I am against thee, O Gog, the chief prince of Meshech and Tubal: And I will turn thee back, and put hooks into thy jaws, and I will bring thee forth, and all thine army,**

horses and horsemen, all of them clothed with all sorts of armour, even a great company with bucklers and shields, all of them handling swords: Persia, Ethiopia, and Libya with them; all of them with shield and helmet (Ezekiel 38:1–5).

When the massive worldwide earthquake takes place and destroys all the major cities, it doesn't destroy Jerusalem but rather splits it into three parts to create a vast valley— the one the Bible says will be the site of the Battle of Armageddon. **And he gathered them together into a place called in the Hebrew tongue Armageddon** (Revelation 16:16).

The nations have been preparing for this war to end all wars for many years, and it's now beginning as Russia and her allies viciously attack Israel to take a spoil and rob her of everything—produce, livestock, businesses, silver, gold and any other type of material wealth they can. Russia wants to completely destroy Israel's infrastructure and its people, but she doesn't know God is going to fight for Israel as the Bible says He will. **Behold, I am against thee, O Gog** (Ezekiel 38:3).

The people of Russia consider their leader to be a great general, but the Lord is completely against him. Nevertheless, many other nations begin siding with him—nations such as Persia [Iran], Ethiopia and Libya. They all band together and storm into Israel with millions of soldiers riding on war horses and carrying bucklers and shields.

When Jesus was on Earth, He knew this war was coming; and He had warned people about it. He said it would be so violent and destructive that unless the days were shortened, not one person would survive. **For then shall be great tribulation, such as was not since the beginning of the world to this time, no, nor ever shall be. And except those days should be shortened, there should no flesh be saved** (Matthew 24:21,22).

Concerning the Russian leader, the Lord said, **And I will turn thee back, and put hooks into thy jaws** (Ezekiel 38:4). God is all-powerful, and Russia and her allies have no idea what an angry God is capable of doing. They're in for the greatest shock of their lives!

Thou shalt ascend and come like a storm, thou shalt be like a cloud to cover the land, thou, and all thy bands, and many people with thee. Thus saith the Lord GOD; It shall also come to pass, that at the same time shall things come into thy mind, and thou shalt think an evil thought: And thou shalt say, I will go up to the land of unwalled villages; I will go to them that are at rest, that dwell safely, all of them dwelling without walls, and having neither bars nor gates, To take a spoil, and to take a prey; to turn thine hand upon the desolate places that are now inhabited, and upon the people that are gathered out of the nations, which have gotten cattle and goods, that dwell in the midst of the land (Ezekiel 38:9–12).

Russia and her allies brutally besiege the little country of Israel with not one drop of mercy, and they take everything they can get their hands on. There are so many soldiers involved in the attack that they cover the land like a ravaging cloud. Israel isn't expecting or ready for this and has built no walls to keep the attackers out; so the enemy completely pillages every city, town and village. God had given the Israelites, His people, the wisdom and knowledge to make their country prosper; and Russia wants all of that prosperity that she can get. She thinks she has it made, but God has other plans...deadly ones.

And thou shalt come from thy place out of the north parts, thou, and many people with thee, all of them riding upon horses, a great company, and a mighty army: And thou shalt come up against my people of Israel, as a cloud to cover the land; it shall be in the latter days, and I will bring thee against my land, that the heathen may know me, when I shall be sanctified in thee, O Gog, before their eyes (Ezekiel 38:15,16). The enemy thinks they're raiding Israel of their own accord, but God is the one who has drawn them there. He's getting millions of them exactly where He wants them; they're falling right into the trap He has laid. *Thus saith the Lord, I will bring you against my land.*

As things begin to heat up, the people of the

world are going to soon discover that God is the one and only true God. Millions have already witnessed and fallen victim to His greatness when the angels' trumpets sounded, and He rained down judgments too horrible to even imagine. Now, God is going to finish making good on every prophecy He has ever given to His holy men of old.

Thus saith the Lord GOD; Art thou he of whom I have spoken in old time by my servants the prophets of Israel, which prophesied in those days many years that I would bring thee against them? And it shall come to pass at the same time when Gog shall come against the land of Israel, saith the Lord GOD, that my fury shall come up in my face. For in my jealousy and in the fire of my wrath have I spoken, Surely in that day there shall be a great shaking in the land of Israel; So that the fishes of the sea, and the fowls of the heaven, and the beasts of the field, and all creeping things that creep upon the earth, and all the men that are upon the face of the earth, shall shake at my presence, and the mountains

shall be thrown down, and the steep places shall fall, and every wall shall fall to the ground (Ezekiel 38:17–20). Once God has successfully drawn the countries from the North to Israel, His fury explodes in His face; and the battle begins. Not one soldier has the slightest idea of what an angry God has in store for them.

Suddenly, the Earth begins to shake due to the mighty presence of God, and every person and creature can feel it. Walls, buildings and even huge mountains fall to the ground as if they're just mere pieces of paper. The roles are beginning to reverse; the enemy soldiers are terrified...and they have no place to hide. God is now fighting for Israel just like He did in Old Testament days but on a much greater scale.

And I will call for a sword against him throughout all my mountains, saith the Lord GOD: every man's sword shall be against his brother (Ezekiel 38:21). Russia and her allies have been so proud of their vicious attack on Israel and are already declaring victory until the scene suddenly turns into one of total chaos for them. The soldiers are so overcome with fear that they lose all allegiance and begin fighting their own countrymen. It's each man for himself.

And I will plead against him with pestilence and with blood; and I will rain upon him, and upon his bands, and upon the many people that are with him, an overflowing rain, and great hailstones, fire, and brimstone. Thus will I magnify myself, and sanctify myself; and I will be known in the eyes of many nations, and they shall know that I am the LORD (Ezekiel 38:22,23). When the witnesses were on Earth, fire had come out of their mouths; but now fire and brimstone are raining down from Heaven, and there is no escape. People everywhere become like human torches, running around with their bodies on fire until they're burned to death. The bloodcurdling cries sound like a choir from hell itself.

God is proving to the world that He is God. **For I am the LORD: I will speak, and the word that I shall speak shall come to pass** (Ezekiel 12:25). Just as Pharaoh had learned that the Lord was God Almighty when He drowned the magnificent Egyptian army in the Red Sea, the entire world is now getting that same message loud and clear. They had been warned before, but they didn't listen; so now they're living a real nightmare of terror.

Therefore, thou son of man, prophesy against Gog, and say, Thus saith the Lord GOD; Behold, I am against thee, O Gog, the chief prince of Meshech and Tubal: And I will turn thee back, and leave but the sixth part of thee, and will cause thee to come up from the north parts, and will bring thee upon the mountains of Israel (Ezekiel 39:1,2). God holds nothing back. His mighty arm of judgment is lifted so high that only one-sixth of Russia and her allies are left.

And I will smite thy bow out of thy left hand, and will cause thine arrows to fall out of thy right hand. Thou shalt fall upon the mountains of Israel, thou, and all thy bands, and the people that is with thee: I will give thee unto the ravenous birds of every sort, and to the beasts of the field to

be devoured. **Thou shalt fall upon the open field: for I have spoken it, saith the Lord GOD** (Ezekiel 39:3–5). God draws thousands of highly trained soldiers into the mountains and knocks their powerful war weapons out of their hands with just the sound of His voice. Most of the soldiers have already died, and the one-sixth who are left are completely helpless. God hasn't just defeated Russia and her allies; He has completely obliterated them, and ravenous birds and vicious beasts devour the bodies.

And I will send a fire on Magog, and among them that dwell carelessly in the isles: and they shall know that I am the LORD. So will I make my holy name known in the midst of my people Israel; and I will not let them pollute my holy name any more: and the heathen shall know that I am the LORD, the Holy One in Israel. Behold, it is come, and it is done, saith the Lord GOD; this is the day whereof I have spoken (Ezekiel 39:6–8). God makes one final statement to these countries by raining down fire on their homelands. Never before has a fire consumed an entire city, let alone several countries. Multitudes die while others lie in the streets covered with burns and shrieking in excruciating pain, but there is nowhere to get help or relief of any kind.

Never before has there been such a massive slaughter, and the cleanup has to begin; but the people of Israel don't even know where to start. The aftermath is worse than if many nuclear bombs had gone off.

And they that dwell in the cities of Israel shall go forth, and shall set on fire and burn the weapons, both the shields and the bucklers, the bows and the arrows, and the handstaves, and the spears, and they shall burn them with fire seven years: So that they shall take no wood out of the field, neither cut down any out of the forests; for they shall burn the weapons with fire (Ezekiel 39:9,10). The people begin burning the thousands and thousands of war weapons that are left, not knowing that it will take seven years to finish the job. They won't have to cut down one tree for use as fuel or energy throughout the entire seven-year cleanup.

And they shall spoil those that spoiled them, and rob those that robbed them, saith the Lord GOD. And it shall come to pass in that day, that I will give unto Gog a place there of graves in Israel, the valley of the passengers on the east of the sea: and it shall stop the noses of the passengers: and there shall they bury Gog and all his multitude: and they shall call it The valley of Hamon-gog. And seven months shall the house of Israel be burying of them, that they may cleanse the land. Yea, all the people of the land shall bury them; and it shall be to them a renown the day that I shall be glorified, saith the Lord GOD (Ezekiel 39:10–13). Russia and her arrogant allies had enjoyed every minute of robbing and pillaging the Israelites, and now the Israelites are doing the same thing to them.

And they shall sever out men of continual employment, passing through the land to bury with the passengers those that remain upon the face of the earth, to cleanse it: after the end of seven months shall they

search (Ezekiel 39:14). In addition to burning all of the war weapons, Israel faces the overwhelming task of burying all of the dead—a disgusting and thankless job that will take them seven months to complete. The valley where the battle took place is soon to become the largest cemetery in the history of civilization because there are literally millions of bodies to dispose of. For some, burying bodies becomes their only job for seven months; but the task is so mammoth that all of the people of Israel have to help in one way or another.

The whole situation is completely revolting, and the stench is nauseating; but the Bible said the land must be cleansed—not one bone can remain. **And the passengers that pass through the land, when any seeth a man's bone, then shall he set up a sign by it, till the buriers have buried it in the valley of Hamon-gog. And also the name of the city shall be Hamonah. Thus shall they cleanse the land** (Ezekiel 39:15,16). If anyone finds even one bone, it must be marked with a sign until it's buried. Not until the land is completely cleansed will God be glorified.

And, thou son of man, thus saith the Lord GOD; Speak unto every feathered fowl, and to every beast of the field, Assemble yourselves, and come; gather yourselves on every side to my sacrifice that I do sacrifice for you, even a great sacrifice upon the mountains of Israel, that ye may eat flesh, and drink blood. Ye shall eat the flesh of the mighty, and drink the blood of the princes of the earth, of rams, of lambs, and of goats, of bullocks, all of them fatlings of Bashan. And ye shall eat fat till ye be full, and drink blood till ye be drunken, of my sacrifice which I have sacrificed for you. Thus ye shall be filled at my table with horses and chariots, with mighty men, and with all men of war, saith the Lord GOD (Ezekiel 39:17–20). God Himself calls every bird and beast to a huge feast of human flesh, to devour the millions of rotting bodies covering the valley like a thick shroud of death. He wants them to eat the flesh and drink the blood of those who were once greedy and powerful in the eyes of the world but are now nothing...and in the eyes of God, that's all they ever were.

And I will set my glory among the heathen, and all the heathen shall see my judgment that I have executed, and my hand that I have laid upon them. So the house of Israel shall know that I am the LORD their God from that day and forward. And the heathen shall know that the house of Israel went into captivity for their iniquity: because they trespassed against me, therefore hid I my face from them, and gave them into the hand of their enemies: so fell they all by the sword. According to their uncleanness and according to their transgressions have I done unto them, and hid my face from them (Ezekiel 39:21–24). The whole world sees what has happened to Russia and her allies, and people have to admit that only the judgments of God could have caused such total and utter death and destruction. Many also begin to understand that all of the persecutions Israel has faced for thousands of years has been because of their sin and disobedience and their rejection of

Christ. God could never move for His people as He had wanted to for all of those years.

Israel is so relieved that this great battle with Russia and her allies is over...but Peter and the other Christians know that this is just the beginning. When all of the other nations see what has happened, they begin flocking to Israel by the millions from all over the world.

John the Revelator said, **And I saw three unclean spirits like frogs come out of the mouth of the dragon, and out of the mouth of the beast, and out of the mouth of the false prophet. For they are the spirits of devils, working miracles, which go forth unto the kings of the earth and of the whole world, to gather them to the battle of that great day of God Almighty** (Revelation 16:13,14). Devils can appear in many forms, and spirits of the devil go into the leaders of the goat nations of the world to draw them to the battle while God's Spirit draws the sheep nations; and they all rush in to take their places.

God had already dried up the Euphrates

River to make a way for the kings of the East, China and Japan, to come to Jerusalem; and they are now on their way. Never has there been such a mass movement of armies, and the world watches spellbound at what's going on and wonders what can possibly be coming next.

God had carefully planned this war to be one of all nations, and God's many prophecies about that fact are coming true. Whether they know it or not, all those who have not and will not believe or receive His prophecies are doomed. **And if any man shall take away from the words of the book of this prophecy, God shall take away his part out of the book of life, and out of the holy city, and from the things which are written in this book** (Revelation 22:19).

As other nations arrive, the battle continues; and it's like a mighty magnet because more and more nations keep coming. **Proclaim ye this among the Gentiles; Prepare war, wake up the mighty men, let all the men of war draw near; let them come up** (Joel 3:9).

The nations are not just coming; they're

arriving well-prepared to do battle. People are even turning everyday work tools into war weapons. **Beat your plowshares into swords and your pruninghooks into spears: let the weak say, I am strong** [for the great war]. **Assemble yourselves, and come, all ye heathen, and gather yourselves together round about: thither cause thy mighty ones to come down, O LORD. Put ye in the sickle, for the harvest is ripe: come, get you down; for the press is full, the vats overflow; for their wickedness is great. Multitudes, multitudes in the valley of decision: for the day of the LORD is near in the valley of decision** (Joel 3:10,11,13,14). Multitudes of people have never wanted Jesus, and they never will. They've rejected their last chance to accept Him, and now there is no mercy left for them.

For, behold, in those days, and in that time, when I shall bring again the captivity of Judah and Jerusalem, I will also gather all nations, and will bring them down into the valley of Jehoshaphat, and will plead with them there for my people and for my

**heritage Israel, whom they have scattered
among the nations, and parted my land**
(Joel 3:1,2). Now, every nation under the sun
has either arrived or is still making its way to
Jerusalem; and God is going to make them
pay dearly for what they have done to Him,
His Son, His people and His land. They will
soon regret ever setting foot in Israel.

**Behold, I will make Jerusalem a cup
of trembling unto all the people round
about, when they shall be in the siege
both against Judah and against Jerusalem.
And in that day will I make Jerusalem a
burdensome stone for all people: all that
burden themselves with it shall be cut in
pieces, though all the people of the earth
be gathered together against it** (Zechariah
12:2,3). The battle continues to grow in size
and intensity; and finally, all of the nations
are gathered against Jerusalem...and the worst
is yet to come. The armies of the nations are
going to wish they had never heard of that
city because most of them will be destroyed
there.

At first, all the goat nations rejoice because

it looks like Israel is going down in defeat. They're completely outnumbered; and soon, two-thirds of the Jews are dead...but it's all a part of God's plan. **And it shall come to pass, that in all the land, saith the LORD, two parts therein shall be cut off and die; but the third shall be left therein** (Zechariah 13:8).

No matter how hard the Jews battle, only one-third of them remain to continue fighting the deadliest and most destructive war they have ever faced. Only those who have accepted Jesus as their Lord and Savior survive, and the Lord had said He would purify them. **And I will bring the third part through the fire, and will refine them as silver is refined, and will try them as gold is tried: they shall call on my name, and I will hear them: I will say, It is my people: and they shall say, The LORD is my God** (Zechariah 13:9). At last, the Lord not only calls the Jews His people; but He rejoices in saying, "I am yours."

With all of the hindrances out of the way, the Lord can finally fight for the Jews as He has always wanted to; and the battle takes a drastic turn. The long-awaited day of the Lord has arrived—the third appearance of Christ. **Behold, he cometh with clouds; and every eye shall see him, and they also which pierced him: and all kindreds of the earth shall wail because of him. Even so, Amen** (Revelation 1:7). Jesus, the only Savior of the world, appears suspended in midair for the whole world to see; and no words can describe such a sight of pure divinity.

This is not the gentle, merciful Christ who has offered Himself to the world for so long; He's now the ferocious Lion of the Tribe of Judah, and He's ready for the war to end all wars. Jesus said there has never been a war like this one, but He also said there would never be another one like it. **For in those days shall be affliction, such as was not from the beginning of the creation which God created unto this time, neither shall be** (Mark 13:19).

And I saw heaven opened, and behold a white horse; and he that sat upon him was called Faithful and True, and in

righteousness he doth judge and make war (Revelation 19:11). The world is breathless— they don't know what to expect from such an awesome yet angry and formidable-looking Christ.

For as the lightning cometh out of the east, and shineth even unto the west; so shall also the coming of the Son of man be (Matthew 24:27). Jesus doesn't come into the world silently as He did the first two times He came. He comes as a bolt of lightning that darkens every light source known to man. People all over the world can't block out the sight of this raging Christ. **For wheresoever the carcase is, there will the eagles be gathered together** (Matthew 24:28). The carcass is the false doctrines of the world, and the eagles are the intellectuals who have refused to recognize the truths of Jehovah God; and they've all gathered against Jesus.

Immediately after the tribulation of those days shall the sun be darkened, and the moon shall not give her light, and the stars shall fall from heaven, and the powers of the heavens shall be shaken: And then

shall appear the sign of the Son of man in heaven: and then shall all the tribes of the earth mourn, and they shall see the Son of man coming in the clouds of heaven with power and great glory (Matthew 24:29,30). The surviving Jews behold the sight of their true Messiah, and the world looks on in awe as they all fall on their faces and cry agonizing tears of such overwhelming sorrow and shame that it's as though they have all lost their firstborn.

The majority of the world can't understand what's going on; but when the surviving Jews realize that they have put Jesus and His Father through years of disappointment and rejection and that they had crucified their true Messiah, it's almost more than they can take. **And I will pour upon the house of David, and upon the inhabitants of Jerusalem, the spirit of grace and of supplications: and they shall look upon me whom they have pierced, and they shall mourn for him, as one mourneth for his only son, and shall be in bitterness for him, as one that is in bitterness for his firstborn** (Zechariah 12:10).

Although the battle is raging all around them, the Jews continue weeping uncontrollably in utter despair and humiliation. They finally realize what they have missed for 2000 years by not accepting the loving Christ, the Lamb of God who loved them so much that He died and gave His very blood for them. Even after all they have put Him through, the Jews are completely humbled to realize that He's still showing them mercy.

Jesus remains suspended in midair with the battle in full force below Him until the whole world has taken a good look, and then He and the armies of Heaven go into action. **The LORD also shall roar out of Zion, and utter his voice from Jerusalem; and the heavens and the earth shall shake: but the LORD will be the hope of his people, and the strength of the children of Israel** (Joel 3:16).

Jesus comes thundering down with such force and power that it's as if a massive landslide has hit the whole Earth, and He's on a mission to rid the world of all wicked humanity once and for all. At last, Israel has hope; and all the strength of divinity is fighting for them.

Man has bragged for years about all the destructive war weapons he has spent so much time and money creating and producing; but now it's all such a waste. All of the world's most powerful weapons put together are nothing compared to what awaits in Heaven's arsenal. The people of the world thought they had seen it all when the Russian army and its allies were annihilated, but that doesn't even begin to compare to what Jesus now begins to pour out.

People fear that the entire world will soon be destroyed, and the angels freely and constantly declare that the people of the world deserve what God is serving them for their many wicked years of arrogance, disrespect, disobedience and sin. God had warned that He could hate as much as He could love, and God's hate is now in full force against all those who have blasphemed His holy name and worshiped the Beast. Men are dying like flies as unimaginable judgments of mass destruction fall all over the Earth. Multitudes are being crushed, torn apart and incinerated.

People don't know what to do as they now realize they have no chance against this Christ of fury. Those who are still alive run for the mountains, begging for them to fall on them and hide them from the terrifying Lion of the Tribe of Judah who is pouring out death and destruction without one drop of mercy. **And the kings of the earth, and the great men, and the rich men, and the chief captains, and the mighty men, and every bondman, and every free man, hid themselves in the dens and in the rocks of the mountains; And said to the mountains and rocks, Fall on us, and hide us from the face of him that sitteth on the throne, and from the wrath of the Lamb: For the great day of his wrath is come; and who shall be able to stand** (Revelation 6:15–17)?

Then shall the LORD go forth, and fight against those nations, as when he fought in the day of battle. And his feet shall stand in that day upon the mount of Olives, which is before Jerusalem on the east, and the mount of Olives shall cleave in the midst thereof toward the east and toward the

west, and there shall be a very great valley; and half of the mountain shall remove toward the north, and half of it toward the south. And ye shall flee to the valley of the mountains; for the valley of the mountains shall reach unto Azal: yea, ye shall flee, like as ye fled from before the earthquake in the days of Uzziah king of Judah: and the LORD my God shall come, and all the saints with thee** (Zechariah 14:3–5). When Jesus comes down to do battle, He stands upon the Mount of Olives like a great warrior; and the whole mountain splits in two. Never before has the world seen such an incredible sight.

The ground is completely covered with a putrid blanket of dead bodies that are maimed beyond recognition, and human blood flows up to the horses' bridles for 200 miles; but God no longer cares. **And the winepress was trodden without the city, and blood came out of the winepress, even unto the horse bridles, by the space of a thousand and six hundred furlongs** (Revelation 14:20).

Jesus had come and shed His blood to save

all who would accept it, but most had rejected it; so no amount of human bloodshed is too much to avenge for such a sacrifice. God has no love or mercy left. Sinful mankind made their final choice and blasphemed against the Holy Spirit of God, and God is making sure that they will never forget it as multitudes find themselves burning in the lake of fire, never to escape for all eternity.

The terrifying sight of a furious Jesus trampling the Earth in vengeance is enough to give anyone an instant heart attack. **His eyes were as a flame of fire, and on his head were many crowns** [showing He has all power]; **and he had a name written, that no man knew, but he himself. And he was clothed with a vesture dipped in blood: and his name is called The Word of God. And the armies which were in heaven followed him upon white horses, clothed in fine linen, white and clean. And out of his mouth goeth a sharp sword, that with it he should smite the nations** (Revelation 19:12–15). Christ's flaming eyes penetrate right into the very souls of people as He viciously destroys everyone in His path with a deadly sword that comes out of His mouth.

And he shall rule them with a rod of iron: and he treadeth the winepress of the fierceness and wrath of Almighty God. And he hath on his vesture and on his thigh a name written, KING OF KINGS, AND LORD OF LORDS (Revelation 19:15,16). The Lord's name is clearly written and displayed for all to see. Never again will there be a question as to who He is.

When Jesus and His army of angels and the saints of God land right in the middle of the bloody war zone, they instantly render the devil and what's left of his army helpless. Heaven is in complete control and pouring out nothing but endless death and destruction.

Who is this that cometh from Edom, with dyed garments from Bozrah? this that is glorious in his apparel, travelling in the greatness of his strength? I that speak in righteousness, mighty to save (Isaiah 63:1). Jesus shows the world His mighty power and strength, and it's clear that nothing can defeat Him.

Wherefore art thou red in thine apparel, and thy garments like him that treadeth in the winevat? I have trodden the winepress alone; and of the people there was none with me: for I will tread them in mine anger, and trample them in my fury; and their blood shall be sprinkled upon my garments, and I will stain all my raiment. For the day of vengeance is in mine heart, and the year of my redeemed is come (Isaiah 63:2–4). Blood is flying everywhere, and Christ's garments are covered with it. His unquenchable wrath is heartless towards those who have the Mark of the Beast for they have blasphemed against the Holy Ghost, and they mean nothing to Him. **These shall make war with the Lamb, and the Lamb shall overcome them: for he is Lord of lords, and King of kings: and they that are with him are called, and chosen, and faithful** (Revelation 17:14).

As the battle starts to wind down somewhat, an angel calls all of the birds and animals to yet another bloody, human banquet—one which includes the fresh flesh of mutilated kings, captains and princes. **And I saw an**

angel standing in the sun; and he cried with a loud voice, saying to all the fowls that fly in the midst of heaven, Come and gather yourselves together unto the supper of the great God; That ye may eat the flesh of kings, and the flesh of captains, and the flesh of mighty men, and the flesh of horses, and of them that sit on them, and the flesh of all men, both free and bond, both small and great. And the remnant were slain with the sword of him that sat upon the horse, which sword proceeded out of his mouth: and all the fowls were filled with their flesh (Revelation 19:17,18,21).

In the midst of all this bloodshed, the Lord doesn't forget the devil-man, the Beast. **And I saw the beast, and the kings of the earth, and their armies, gathered together to make war against him** [Jesus] **that sat on the horse, and against his army** [with Him]. **And the beast was taken** (Revelation 19:19,20). The Beast has blasphemed the very God of Heaven and spit in His eye again and again, doing nothing but the will of the devil. He even declared himself to be God, and his time of doom has finally come.

The Beast has lied to the entire world and has never really cared for even one soul; so cheers erupt all around the world when Jesus shouts, "Cast him into the lake of fire, burning with fire and brimstone." **And the beast was taken, and with him the false prophet that wrought miracles before him, with which he deceived them that had received the mark of the beast, and them that worshipped his image. These both were cast alive into a lake of fire burning with brimstone** (Revelation 19:20).

Jesus casts the false prophet into the lake of fire right along with the Beast because he's just as wicked as the Beast. He had deceived many people into taking the Mark, made an image of the Beast and forced people to bow down and worship it or be killed. The Bible says that the devil will be cast into the same lake of fire and eternal torture right after the close of the Perfect Age.

After Jesus gets rid of the Beast once and for all, He forces the nations into the valley of Jehoshaphat and then judges them for how they have treated the Jews. **Let the heathen be wakened, and come up to the valley of Jehoshaphat: for there will I sit to judge all the heathen round about** (Joel 3:12). Never before has there been a worldwide trial or one in which a guilty verdict brings eternal damnation.

Jesus and His armies from Heaven destroy every one of the goat nations—those who have persecuted the Jews, made them slaves and mercilessly killed millions of them. He allows the sheep nations to survive because they have been good to God's chosen people down through the years. **And Enoch also, the seventh from Adam, prophesied of these, saying, Behold, the Lord cometh with ten thousands of his saints, To execute judgment upon all, and to convince all that are ungodly among them of all their ungodly deeds which they have ungodly committed, and of all their hard speeches which ungodly sinners have spoken against him** (Jude 1:14,15).

While the battle rages in Israel, the rest of the world is not being spared. Angels continue to pour out plagues all over the world, devastating entire nations and killing billions. **Behold, the LORD maketh the earth empty, and maketh it waste, and turneth it upside down, and scattereth abroad the inhabitants thereof. The earth also is defiled under the inhabitants thereof; because they have transgressed the laws, changed the ordinance, broken the everlasting covenant. Therefore hath the curse devoured the earth, and they that dwell therein are desolate: therefore the inhabitants of the earth are burned, and few men left** (Isaiah 24:1,5,6). The vast majority of those who thought they could survive the Tribulation Period have now lifted up their eyes in either Heaven or hell.

The plagues pouring down on the Earth like massive waterfalls are so heinous and completely beyond human comprehension that flesh actually melts right off people's bones, and their eyes disintegrate in their sockets. **And this shall be the plague wherewith the LORD will smite all the people that have fought against Jerusalem; Their flesh shall**

consume away while they stand upon their feet, and their eyes shall consume away in their holes, and their tongue shall consume away in their mouth (Zechariah 14:12).

Many of the nations had been deceived into thinking they could actually win this war, but no one had ever seen anything like the world-wide annihilation they had just witnessed. **The foundations of the earth do shake. The earth is utterly broken down, the earth is clean dissolved, the earth is moved exceedingly. The earth shall reel to and fro like a drunkard, and shall be removed like a cottage; and the transgression thereof shall be heavy upon it; and it shall fall, and not rise again** (Isaiah 24:18–20). The Earth is so completely destroyed that it's beyond recognition. The Lord's wrath has ravaged it with such force that it's actually reeling and rocking, and those who are left are petrified as the Earth moves under them.

Peter had watched the entire battle from start to finish, and now he's completely numb. He has no words to describe what he has seen or the complete and utter devastation left behind.

All that he had ever read and studied about for so long took place right before his very eyes, and he's so thankful to the Lord that he's still alive. He never imagined the end of the known world would look like this.

The crucified Christ came, conquered and won; and He cast all those with the Mark into the lake of fire for eternity. What a horrible end for all who had rejected the Lord...but each person had made his or her own final choice. The screams of the damned will forever go up from the pits of hell, "We're so tormented! We're lost! We're damned to this burning hell for all eternity! There will never be any hope of deliverance for us!"

Oh, what weeping and wailing there was as they were cast into the lake of fire to be tormented forever and ever! The Lion of the Tribe of Judah doesn't care anymore. He has only hate for them. Yes, as God had said, He can hate as much as He can love. Now, they're in the lake of fire and brimstone with the Beast and the Antispirit. What a price that they must pay for selling their souls to the devil...lost, lost forevermore!

About the Author

Reverend Ernest Angley is the pastor and founder of Ernest Angley Ministries with churches in two locations: Ernest Angley's Grace Cathedral in Cuyahoga Falls, Ohio and Grace Cathedral in Akron, Ohio. This Jesus ministry is in the midst of a tremendous worldwide outreach which is spreading the Gospel into many nations by way of crusades, television and the printed page. God has endowed Reverend Angley with special gifts to bring healing for soul, mind and body to people all over the world. He does not claim to be a healer but a witness to the marvelous healing power of Christ. His television programs—"The Ernest Angley Hour" (aired weekly) and "The Ninety and Nine Club" (aired daily)—present the fullness of God's Word and teach the truth about salvation, healing and the baptism in the Holy Ghost.

Check your local listing for times in your area.

You are Special To God

Visit our website at www.ernestangley.org

MORE BOOKS

by Ernest Angley

RAPTURED

A novel by Ernest Angley about the second coming of Christ based on biblical facts. This timely book could change your life. Price: $3.50

FAITH IN GOD HEALS THE SICK

An instructive book by Ernest Angley telling not only how to receive physical healing from the Lord, but also how to keep that healing. Price: $1.95

UNTYING GOD'S HANDS

With amazing frankness the author has dealt with many controversial subjects in this book: the ministry of angels, preparation required for the Rapture, guidelines for dating, sex in marriage, sex outside marriage, masturbation, homosexuality. Many other subjects covering the whole life of man are woven into the underlying theme of how to untie God's hands. Price: $10.00

CELL 15

The dramatic true story of the imprisonment of Reverend Ernest Angley in Munich, Germany, for preaching the Gospel and praying for the sick. Price: $2.95

GOD'S RAINBOW OF PROMISES

Precious promises from the Word of God (KJV) to cover your every need now and forever will enhance your personal devotions and prove a great blessing in time of trouble. Price: $1.95

THE DECEIT OF LUCIFER

Using the Word of God as the only standard, Reverend Angley strips the camouflage of Lucifer's insidious deceit from demonology, seducing spirits and the counterfeit works of God. A culmination of information derived from years of training by the Holy Spirit, this book is a must for anyone who wishes to recognize the deadly pitfalls of the dangerous end-time hour in which we live. Price: $10.00

LEECHING OF THE MIND

Like parasitic leeches of the jungle that live off the blood of their victims, leeches of the mind sap the life force of reason. Through the gifts of the Holy Spirit, Reverend Angley exposes the inner working of Lucifer in the human mind, revealing the most incredible takeover by Lucifer a person could suffer other than total devil possession of the soul. Price: $10.00

THE POWER OF BIBLE FASTING

The Power Of Bible Fasting is one of the most thorough books on Bible fasting ever written, an invaluable guide into a deeper walk with God and the reality of His presence. Price: $10.00

LOVE IS THE ROAD

Through His great and precious promises we receive much from the Lord on His Love Road. The Love Road is a supernatural Road laid out by supernatural power, planned by the Lord God Almighty. Discover how you, too, can walk this marvelous Road into the fullness and greatness of God in this last and final hour. Price: $10.00

WEEDS IN EDEN

One of God's greatest disappointments: Finding weeds in Eden. *Weeds in Eden* describes the cost to God and man of minds overrun with the weeds of disobedience and rebellion. The price paid by Heaven and Earth was sorrow, heartache and despair, and the price today is still the same. Let this book help you search out any weeds that would contaminate the Eden of your mind in this last and final hour. Price: **$10.00**

THE UNFORGIVABLE SIN

There is a sin not even Calvary can pardon. Once people commit this sin, only doom and damnation await them with no chance ever of heaven. Jesus said, *All manner of sin and blasphemy shall be forgiven unto men, but the blasphemy against the Holy Ghost shall not be forgiven unto men . . . neither in this world, neither in the world to come* (Matthew 12:31, 32) Price: **$10.00**

REALITY OF THE BLOOD: VOL. 1

In this enlightened book on divine blood, the unique and insightful author, through the power of the Holy Ghost, opens up amazing revelations about the importance of the blood of Jesus for all people. Those who love God with all their heart will be thrilled to find the marvelous understanding of the blood that has been set down in this book. Price: **$10.00**

PROSPERITY: SPIRITUAL, PHYSICAL, FINANCIAL...

To bring forth the fullness of God's prosperity that we find in His divine will, the writer has gone into the deepness of the Holy Spirit and the Word of God. Prosperity for soul, mind and body is God's will for all His Children. Price: **$10.00**

REALITY OF THE BLOOD: VOL. 2
They used the Blood . . . We must use the Blood

The power in the divine blood of Jesus is being presented in living reality as multitudes experience miracles of healing for soul, mind and body. The Early Church used divine blood through the power of the Holy Ghost, now it's time for the Church in this last and final hour to use the power in the divine blood. Price: **$10.00**

REALITY OF THE BLOOD: VOL. 3
Faith and Feelings!
Through the Spirit of God recognize the difference between feelings and faith. Feelings can dishearten you if you rely on them to determine your benefits with God and what you should do for Him. Trusting in feelings is the reason so many Christians have battles of the mind. Price: $**10.00**

REALITY OF THE BLOOD: VOL. 4
Blood Victory Over Disappointments!
Realize what is yours through divine blood: freedom from depression, oppression, sin, sickness, disease and all other bondages of the devil. Through divine blood it is possible to overcome Satan's great weapon of disappointments and take on the mind of Jesus. Price: $**10.00**

THE REALITY OF THE PERSON OF THE HOLY SPIRIT: VOL. 1
The Holy Spirit in Types and Shadows
Reverend Angley lifts the mist curtains of the Old Testament to reveal the Holy Spirit in types and shadows. Let these marvelous types and shadows come alive in your heart and thrill your very being. Price: $**10.00**

THE REALITY OF THE PERSON OF THE HOLY SPIRIT: VOL. 2
The Holy Spirit and Fire
The fire of the Holy Spirit includes great miracles of deliverance as well as the devouring fire of judgment. Read how the fire of the Holy Spirit will affect your life. Price: $**10.00**

THE REALITY OF THE PERSON OF THE HOLY SPIRIT: VOL. 3
The Holy Spirit in the New and Old Testaments
The Holy Spirit worked throughout the New Testament, but did He work in Old Testament days? Yes, He did. Read about it in volume 3 of the Holy Spirit series. Price: $**10.00**

HURRY FRIDAY!
Autobiography of Ernest Angley: Elegant Hardcover Edition
Hurry Friday! will make you laugh, cry, and rejoice in the amazing way God has moved in the life of this unique servant of God. Price: $**30.00**

THE MIND OF CHRIST
Let this mind be in you, which was also in Christ (Philippians 2:5). What made up His mind? Listed in this book are 141 ingredients found in the mind of Christ. Price: $**10.00**

THE REALITY OF THE PERSON OF THE HOLY SPIRIT: VOL. 4
The Mantle of Power
The Bible is filled with examples of the Holy Ghost using the mantle of power through godly men and women. All the truth of God as well as His power is in the mantle. Recognize the blood strength, the greatness, wisdom and knowledge in the glorious mantle of power - and it's for all who will accept it! Price: $**10.00**

LIVING FREE FROM SIN: VOL. 1
Is eternal security conditional or unconditional? Can people really live free from sin? This ground-breaking study delves deep into the Scriptures to shed light on a damnable doctrine spreading throughout the world today and reveals what the Bible really has to say about this subject. Price: $**10.00**

BATTLES OF THE MIND
Are you tormented with Battles of the Mind? Do you fight depression, oppression, despair and mental misgivings? Are you tormented with the past, present and future or bound with stifling doubt and fear? This book gives you the Bible cure for all that Battles Your Mind! Price: $**10.00**

LIVING FREE FROM SIN: VOL. 2

The Bible is filled with the message of Living Free From Sin, and this second volume continues the study of this much-neglected subject. Scripture by scripture, the Lord continues to uncover the damnable doctrine of eternal security in Paul's writings to the Romans, the Corinthians and the Philippians. Price: $**10.00**

REALITY OF THE BLOOD: VOL. 5
Don't Waste The Blood!

Jesus Shed His precious blood on Calvary for a lost and dying world, and He intends for us to use it. That blood is man's most powerful weapon, and we must not waste even one, tiny drop. In this profound end-time teaching, Reverend Angley shares an incredible revelation from the Lord on how to use the divine blood to spray the devil into defeat every day. This book will completely change your life! Price: $**10.00**

HEALING FROM HEAVEN, VOL. 1

God's Word promises healing for soul, mind and body to all people; and that healing comes straight from Heaven. If you're in need of a miracle, this one-of-a-kind miracle manual will show you that you can be made whole. It takes you step-by-step through the different healing methods and then teaches you how to receive and keep your miracle. Price: $**10.00**

Name _____

Address _____

City _____

State _____ Zip _____

PLEASE SEND ME THE BOOKS INDICATED:

Qty. ____ B1 - Raptured - $3.50 ea

Qty. ____ B2 - Faith in God Heals the Sick - $1.95 ea

Qty. ____ B4 - Untying God's Hands - $10.00 ea

Qty. ____ B5 - Cell 15 - $2.95 ea

Qty. ____ B6 - God's Rainbow of Promises - $1.95 ea

Qty. ____ B7 - The Deceit of Lucifer - $10.00 ea

Qty. ____ B8 - Leeching of the Mind - $10.00 ea

Qty. ____ B9 - The Power of Bible Fasting - $10.00 ea

Qty. ____ B10 - Love is the Road - $10.00 ea

Qty. ____ B11 - Weeds In Eden - $10.00 ea

Qty. ____ B12 - The Unforgivable Sin - $10.00 ea

Qty. ____ B13 - Reality of the Blood, Vol. 1 - $10.00 ea

Continued ▶

PLEASE SEND ME THE BOOKS INDICATED:

Qty. ____ B14 - Prosperity: Spiritual, Physical, Financial... - $10.00 ea

Qty. ____ B15 - Reality of the Blood, Vol. 2 - $10.00 ea

Qty. ____ B16 - Reality of the Blood, Vol. 3 - $10.00 ea

Qty. ____ B17 - Reality of the Blood, Vol. 4 - $10.00 ea

Qty. ____ B18 - The Reality of the Person of the Holy Spirit, Vol.1 - $10.00 ea

Qty. ____ B19 - The Reality of the Person of the Holy Spirit, Vol.2 - $10.00 ea

Qty. ____ B20 - Hurry Friday - $30.00 ea

Qty. ____ B22 - The Reality of the Person of the Holy Spirit, Vol.3 - $10.00 ea

Qty. ____ B23 - The Mind of Christ - $10.00 ea

Qty. ____ B24 - The Reality of the Person of the Holy Spirit, Vol.4 - $10.00 ea

Qty. ____ B25 - Living Free From Sin, Vol.1 - $10.00 ea

Qty. ____ B26 - Battles of the Mind - $10.00 ea

Qty. ____ B27 - Living Free From Sin, Vol.2 - $10.00 ea

Qty. ____ B28 - Reality of the Blood, Vol. 5 - $10.00 ea

Qty. ____ B29 - Healing From Heaven, Vol. 1 - $10.00 ea

Qty. ____ B30 - Armageddon - $10.00 ea

Amount enclosed $ _____ (Please No C.O.D.s)

DISTRIBUTORS AND BOOKSTORES ORDER FROM:
WINSTON PRESS, BOX 2091, AKRON, OHIO 44309